MINES OF DARTMOOR
AND THE
TAMAR VALLEY
AFTER 1913

P.H.G. RICHARDSON

DEVON BOOKS

Originally published in 1992 by The Northern Mine Research Society.
This new edition published in 1995 by Devon Books.

British Library Cataloguing in Publication Data
CIP data for this book is available from the British Library

ISBN 0 86114 898 3

DEVON BOOKS
Official Publiser to Devon County Council

Halsgrove House
Lower Moor Way
Tiverton, Devon EX16 6SS
Tel: 01884 243242
Fax: 01884 243325

Printed and bound in Great Britain by The Devonshire Press Ltd, Torquay

Cover illustrations
Some idea of the colossal stopes and timbers required to support them, is gained from these photographs in the Main Lode at Devon Great Consols Mine, taken in 1984. Now flooded to adit level since the pumps stopped at the turn of the century, only a fraction of these extensive workings remain accessible to the mining historian nowadays. *Photos R. H. Bird*

FRONTISPIECE: Stulls or working stagings in the Main Lode, Devon Great Consols Mine. 1984. *Photo R.H. Bird*

CONTENTS

PREFACE

I have written the notes which follow for those, both visitors and residents, who have some awareness of our West Country mining heritage and who would perhaps like to know a little more of the history and significance of the various mining relics they may see; in addition I hope to provide something to interest the more specialised reader. I have kept the notes as far as possible on a personal level, with only minimal dependence on previously published accounts, statistics, etc., most of which are generally available to anyone wishing to consult them, so have relied more on data from less accessible sources and on information which I have myself gathered.

The area covered by the notes is bounded very approximately by the four towns of Okehampton, Chudleigh, Ivybridge and Callington and my original intention was to include all mines in the area which had been worked, or at least had interest shown in them, within the space of my own lifetime (1918 -). But with the recent publication by the University of Exeter of consolidated mineral production, etc., statistics up to the year 1913 for mines of Cornwall, Devon and Somerset, compiled by Dr. Roger Burt and his colleagues, it seemed more logical to alter my starting date to 1914. I have chosen to write about West Devon and East Cornwall because this is the district in which I have always lived so is naturally the area which I know best.

Before ending this preface some further points of detail must be mentioned:-

(i) Many mines were worked under different names at different times, so in such cases I have used what I think to be the best known names.

(ii) When indexing mine names alphabetically I have ignored such prefixes as "Old," "New," "Great," "North," "South," "East," "West," "Wheal," etc.

(iii) Though I have myself worked from the Second Edition Ordnance Survey Six Inches to the Mile maps published in the early 1900s (these being unusually rich in mining details) the notes can be followed quite readily from today's 2½ Inches to the Mile maps with the aid of the National Grid References given in the text.

(iv) As mines occupy *areas* (known as "setts" and which were often quite extensive) whereas Grid References indicate only *points*, I have selected the latter to pinpoint either the centre of a sett or some suitable focal point within it. As all the Grid References quoted in the text bear the same lettered prefix "SX" I have omitted these letters and given only the six figures of the references.

(v) To avoid awkward fractions and decimals I have quoted measurements in pre-metric terms.

(vi) A Glossary of mining terms is included but, to avoid having to refer to this over-often, some explanations are included in the text even at the cost of a certain amount of duplication.

(vii) Though some references may be made to underground workings I have not attempted to describe these in detail as they are exhaustively chronicled in H.G. Dines' 1956 Memoir (see Bibliography). Many such workings are still open and liable to be exceedingly dangerous, so should only be approached or entered by those thoroughly experienced in such explorations. Likewise buildings, flues, chimney stacks, etc., tend by now to be in a very shaky state so that similar caution should also be exercised when in their vicinity. Furthermore, sensible precautions should be taken when visiting old arsenic mines, particularly those where "arsenic burning" has been carried out.

(viii) Mining sites may well be situated on private property so that unless there is clear evidence to the contrary anyone wishing to visit should first seek permission from the owner or lessee. In a few cases I have indicated the present occupiers but these indications are by no means exhaustive and are liable to change anyway.

In conclusion it must be stressed that no notes such as those which follow are ever likely to be complete and final: fresh information comes to light all the time.

ACKNOWLEDGEMENTS

I must first acknowledge the debt I owe to those whose names are given below (some of whom are, alas, no longer with us) also to the staffs of the Maristow Office at Roborough and of the former Bedford Office at Tavistock, for letting me have access to information in their possession and for putting photographs and other documents at my disposal.

Mr. J.B.M. Adams, Ely
Mr. O.A. Baker, Exeter
Mr. R.L. Balkwill, London
Mr. D.B. Barton, Truro
Mr. R. Bayles, Chester
Mr. F.L. Booker, Plymouth
Mrs. B. Brook, Postbridge
Mr. M. Messenger, Cardiff
Capt. C.G. Moor, MA, FRIC, FCS, Kit Hill Mine
Mr. A. Moyle, Gunnislake
Mr. Olver, Golden Dagger Mine
Mr. H.G. Ordish, Blandford
Mr. Osborn, Throwleigh

Mr. J. Brooke, Marazion
Mrs. P. Browning, Tavistock
Dr. R. Burt, University of Exeter
Mr. F. Cloke (per Mrs. H. White, Marytavy)
Mr. J.G. Cloke, Wheal Anna Maria, Tavistock
Mr. A.S. Courtier, Haytor
Mr. & Mrs. P.J. Densham, Totnes
Mr. H.G. Dines, ARSM, AMICE, London
Dr. T.A.P. Greeves, London
Mr. W.A. Grose, Montana, U.S.A. (Per Dr. T.A.P. Greeves)
Mr. F. Higman, Gunnislake
Mr. H. Higman, Devon Great Consols, Tavistock
Mr. J.H. Higman, Gunnislake
Mr. D.J. Hogg, Marytavy
Mr. A.K. Hamilton Jenkin, Redruth
Mrs. F. John, Marytavy
Mr. A. Kendall, Saltash
Mr. Legassick (Sen.), Sheepstor
Major B. Llewellyn, Wheal Josiah, Tavistock
Lt. Cdr. H.H.B. Oswell, R.N., France
Mr. G.C. Pengilly, MBE, ACSM, C.Eng., FIMM, Liskeard
Lt. Col. J.V. Ramsden, CMG, DSO, Honiton
Mr. K.L. Roberts, Shaugh Prior
Mr. P. Roberts, Plymouth
Mr. S. Roberts, Shaugh Prior
Mr. J.A.C. Robins, BEM, Tavistock
Mr. G. Rowe, Victoria, Canada
Mr. D.L. Smith, Brighton
Mr. Stephens, Marytavy (per Lt. Col. T.V. Beer)
Mr. D. Stephens, Ipswich
Mr. C.G. Stone, Aylesbury
Mrs. M. Symons, Wheal Anna Maria, Tavistock
Mr. R.W. Toll, AIMM, Bere Alston
Mr. P.J. Tonkin, Bridford Mine
Mr. E.S. Treseder, Ashburton
Mr. S. Williams, Gunnislake
Mr. W. Wills, Great Rock Mine
Mr. R. Hansford Worth, Plymouth

Chapters 1 to 5 and 11 to 14 have previously appeared in the Journals of the Plymouth Mineral and Mining Club. Additionally Chapter 2 appeared in the quarterly magazine *Dartmoor* and Chapter 11 in *Tamar*, the Journal of the Friends of Morwellham. These chapters are reproduced by kind permission of the editors of those journals.

The maps of Wapsworthy, Hensroost Mine, Wheal Betsy, Ilsington area, Bulkamore Mine, Kit Tin Mine and New Consols Mine are based on the Second Edition Ordnance Survey Six Inch maps of 1904–07 and those of Wheal Friendship and Devon Great Consols Mine on the First Edition Twenty-five Inch maps published in the 1880s.

The photographs and exerpts from the *Western Morning News* are reproduced by kind permission of the Editor and exerpts from the *Totnes Times* are quoted by courtesy of Devon & Cornwall Newspapers Ltd.

Additionally I would like to express my thanks to Owen Baker, Deputy County Librarian, Devon, for his initial suggestion that I might put some of my material into book form and further for reading my manuscript and for making a number of helpful comments and suggestions. Also to Dick Bird, editor, N.M.R.S. Publications, for preparing the manuscript for publication.

Finally I must express my thanks to my wife for persuading me to take the project on in the first place, for encouraging me to see it through to a conclusion and for accepting my inevitable preoccupation with the work while it was being written.

P.H.G. Richardson
Totnes, October, 1991

INTRODUCTION

It may not be out of place to introduce my notes with some sort of explanation of how my interest in local mining, dating from over sixty years ago, began and developed. I should also add that in pre-war years such an interest was regarded as something of an eccentricity, this being before the term "Industrial Archaeology" had been coined; it has since, of course, become a recognised subject worthy of serious study but through lack of general interest in those earlier days much valuable data has been lost.

For unaccountable reasons it seems that I was born with a predilection for ancient mining remains, which first showed itself on a summer holiday at Perranporth in 1925, when I was seven. Apparently disdaining the standard seaside amusements on offer for young children, I pointed out a group of ruinous buildings and chimneys at the end of the beach to the north (Wheal Ramoth?), indicating that I would like to have a closer look, but was told that I must not go near them because they were dangerous, which they probably were.

The following summer we were in a rented cottage at Tremar, north of Liskeard, by which time a more liberal atmosphere must have prevailed, for I remember fearlessly picking wild strawberries growing round the mouths of deep and terrifying shafts at South Caradon Mine and within their perimeter walls. While mining in the area was by that time dead, it had not been dead all that long, so that local inhabitants were still fairly mine-conscious, and I recall being told by our landlord that we ought to walk over to Minions because we could see a traditional Cornish pumping engine there. We duly walked to Minions but as he had omitted to describe the item or tell us its exact location we were uncertain what to look for, though the pump (which must have been at the Prince of Wales Shaft, Phoenix United Mines) was probably staring us in the face. I do, however, have a dim recollection of going into a low and darksome building and seeing in the gloom something which I would today identify as a Cornish or Lancashire boiler but this may be a detail which my imagination has added in retrospect. I did get back to Minions many years later and photographed the Prince of Wales engine house when it was still roofed and in good repair but by then the pumping machinery had been removed.

Summer, 1927, was spent at Hexworthy, on Dartmoor, when it seemed to rain every day though on one apparently non-rainy day I was taken on a walk out to Hensroost Mine, situated a mile south of the Forest Inn and which had only been abandoned a few years before. But not knowing in advance what an interesting place I was going to I did not take my camera, although at that time I had a No. 0 "Brownie" costing about ten shillings (50p) and capable of taking quite good photographs. I got there again in 1934 when luckily everything was still fairly intact and took a number of pictures, some of which are reproduced later in this book, but wish now that I had taken many more.

In 1932 we were at West Blackdown, near Marytavy, from whence expeditions could be made to the several mines in the vicinity, and in that year I began to take some fairly useful pictures, though my knowledge of mining was still almost non-existent — I did not even know that mines had names, still less that any written information about them existed. This at a time when local Geological Survey District Memoirs were still in print at 3/- (15p) a volume and J.H. Collins' classic *West of England Mining Region* at 12/6d (62½p), while Ordnance Survey Six Inches to the Mile maps, each covering an area 3 miles by 2 miles and abounding in mining information were only 2/- (10p) a sheet.

Round about that time I was lent a copy of Rowe's *Perambulation of Dartmoor* which contained among other things a list of local mines extracted from Williams' Mining Directory for 1861 and conveyed the (to me) surprising information that mines had names — hitherto I had merely thought of them as derelict though highly interesting sites — and started me off on the gathering and recording of such names as others of my age might have collected postage stamps or birds' eggs. Even the names themselves had a certain magic about them when read for the first time — Concord, Dippertown, Lydford Consols, Devon New Copper Mines, Ivy Tor, Wheal Frederick and many others.

By the mid 1930s I had discovered via an article by A.K. Hamilton Jenkin in a geographical magazine that much more printed information on West Country mining existed, and so commenced the long search for the standard works on the subject — this was before today's reprints had arrived on the scene — while I also began to build up a complete set of local Ordnance Survey 6-inch maps.

On 24th July 1937, I was taken to Devon Great Consols Mine, four miles west of Tavistock, and once the richest copper mine in Europe. For me this was a memorable day as, although I was by then well aware of the mine's existence, I had not yet seen it and was astonished by its enormous extent. It was in a deserted building there that I found among discarded rubbish the first of a series of tattered notebooks relating to past work at the mine, upon which two subsequent chapters will be based. While I did at least have the wit to recognise that I had come upon a document of uncommon interest I should also have realised at the time, instead of later, that as the "workbook" I had found only covered a three month period it was likely that other similar books could be lying around, for which an immediate search should have been made. Though I failed to do this and many months elapsed before I could make another visit I was fortunate to find that nothing had been disturbed in the meantime and I was able to recover another dozen or so books, covering the years 1922 to 1925. These did not of course relate to the mine's main period of work, which had ended in 1903, but to later small-scale operations, details of which nevertheless proved to be exceedingly interesting.

Subsequent study of the books raised numerous queries, but there was an old miner named Harry Higman who operated a copper precipitating works at Devon Great Consols in the 1930s and early 1940s who, I felt, could have answered at least some of them. At the same time I was reluctant to make my questions to him too specific as I did not want to disclose that I had removed the books even though they had clearly come under the heading of "articles abandoned by their owners." Many years later I discovered that not only could he have given me all the required answers but that he had himself been a foreman on the mine and actually responsible for writing up the books.

By the late 1930s I had acquired a bicycle, which greatly widened my horizons and had I only known of the unbelievable array of historic mining machinery at Wheal Martha (or New Consols Mine), Luckett, which had lain undisturbed since the 1870s and which will be referred to in a later chapter, I could have got over there without difficulty. What a find this would have been for an industrial archaeologist of today and how differently the site would have been treated. As it was, the whole collection was broken up and sold for scrap for a few paltry pounds in 1938.

1939 and the outbreak of war took me away from the West Country for some time and ended the halcyon days of the previous years, when there seemed to have been so much more time for mining explorations and when, prior to the scrap metal drives of the late 1930s, there was so much more of interest to be seen.

Looking back through my diaries, these note failures as well as successes, especially in the earlier years; e.g. failure to look for, notice or interpret many interesting features when they were still in situ and to record their exact locations; failure to photograph noteworthy items properly while wasting film on lesser items, and so on. The early entries reflect not only transport difficulties — we then lived ten miles from important mining areas such as Marytavy and Calstock, and more than once I made the double journey to and from the former place on foot — but also general unpreparedness and lack of equipment, e.g. "Was towed to Marytavy on my bicycle by H— on his motorbike" (this was hazardous, and I believe now illegal, but quicker than walking or ordinary cycling) or — describing entry into an adit at South Devon

United Mine, Petertavy, — "Started wading up in bare feet which was both painful and cold" (not surprising as the month was December).

Despite these shortcomings I did keep some sort of records of what I saw and these I have used when compiling the succeeding notes, which I hope may enable readers to build up something of a picture of former mining activity from today's often scanty remains.

CHAPTER 1

DARTMOOR DIAMONDS?
AN UNUSUAL MINING PROSPECT NEAR WAPSWORTHY
545796

READING IN A SUNDAY NEWSPAPER AN ARTICLE ON jewellery entitled "An Age of Fakes", I was reminded of a chance meeting I had some fifty or more years ago when I was walking over the surface workings of Devon Great Consols Mine.

The newspaper article related to an exhibition of "Synthetic Jewellery and Gems" being held in the Goldsmiths Hall in London, and opened with the statement that imitations of gems have been made for many centuries and that some revered family jewels could well prove to be such, going on to say that natural spinels, white sapphires and zircons can be convincing substitutes for diamonds, adding that only expert testing can distinguish the synthetic gem "zirconia" from diamond.

The chance meeting was with one Jack Cloke who, with his brother Frank, engaged in certain prospecting and mining activity in the district in the earlier part of the century. Both are dead now, Jack having died relatively young while Frank lived until the 1960s. When I met the first-named our conversation was initially about Devon Great Consols itself, concerning which he gave me various interesting information. I was later told that his wife was the daughter of Sam Pengelly, who was a foreman there in the twenties, and whose name features in the work-books referred to in the Introduction and in Chapters 11 and 12.

He told me that he had previously been precipitating copper at Gawton Mine, further down the River Tamar at Grid Ref. 452689 (See Chapter 11 for details of that process) but that he was currently prospecting for zircon and titanium at Wapsworthy, in the parish of Petertavy. His knowledge of the latter minerals was far ahead of mine and I remember him saying that the more valuable titanium minerals were rutile, anatase and brookite, which are pure oxides of titanium, but that the only titanium he had so far found at Wapsworthy was in the form of ilmenite, a combination of titanium, oxygen and iron and of less value.

He seemed unusually interested in zircon which, he said, had many of the physical attributes of diamond, and mentioned the name of a certain titled lady of those days who was said to have been possessed of a very fine diamond tiara, the stones in which Jack had reason to believe were not in fact diamonds but zircons. He kindly offered to take me out to Wapsworthy on the back of his motor cycle (which I think he was repairing when I met him) to see his prospect, but due to other commitments rather than to a lack of confidence in the motor cycle I

Plate I. Jack Cloke's engine at Wapsworthy photographed in 1989.

was unable to accept, and I never saw him again. So apart from making a note of the information he had given me, which had seemed unusual, I put the matter aside pending a chance to investigate further.

Some time afterwards, when I was looking round Gawton Mine, I came upon evidence of fairly recent activity, together with a deserted cottage in which various papers were lying about, including a partly-completed Mines Department form *Annual Report of Output and No. of Persons employed* for the year 1923 in respect of "Gawton Precipitation Works, owner John G. Cloke, Esq." so that part of his narrative certainly checked out.

In 1951, following up a report of some sort of past mining activity on a small tributary of the Youlden Brook, ½ mile E.S.E. of Wapsworthy, I found traces of what appeared likely to have been Jack Cloke's prospect. These consisted of excavations into the old tinners' spoil heaps, a raised launder leading from the excavations towards vestiges of ore-dressing machinery, a Ruston Hornsby engine, a winch and the remains of a hut which had contained assaying equipment including crucibles, sieves and a weighing machine. I was subsequently assured by the late R.W. Toll who, in my experience, was an informant of impeccable reliability, that this was definitely Jack's working and that he did find some zircons.

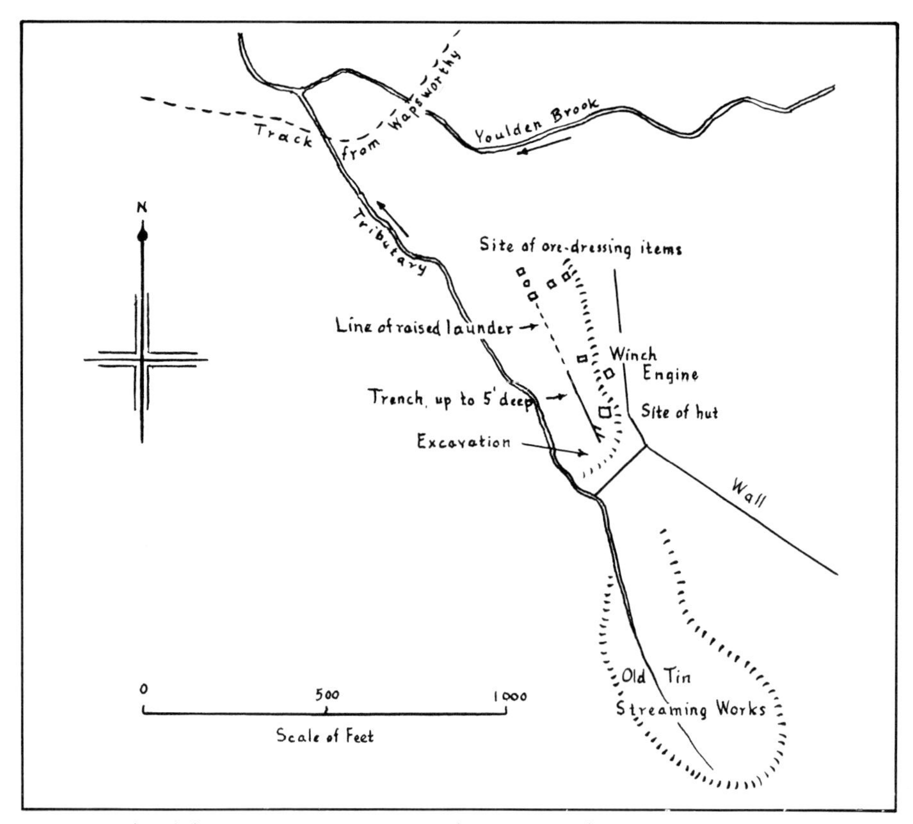

Fig. 1. Jack Cloke's prospect at Wapsworthy as it is today.

Just what had taken him to such a remote spot can only be guessed at, but the probability is that he was looking for tin in the first place and that the zircon discovery may have been unexpected. The presence of zircon in granite is not uncommon and the same goes for ilmenite and even rutile so that any of these might have become concentrated in detritus derived from the nearby granite. Crystals of zircon, which is classed as an obdurate mineral, could have had a better than average chance of surviving such conditions, but whether they would have been of gem quality seems only a possibility.

At the time Jack was at Wapsworthy there was only limited demand for titanium compounds — mostly in connection with paint manufacture — and with large titanium deposits existing around the world (it is the ninth most abundant element in the earth's crust) there would not seem to have been much future in mining ilmenite at such a miniscule prospect as his. Today, however, titanium metal has a place in "high-tech" engineering.

It may be interesting to note that in addition to the artificially-made gem "zirconia," a similar but titanium-based one "titania" was at one time fashionable which was said to have been more brilliant than diamond but lacking the hardness of the latter it was insufficiently resistant to wear.

Walking out to the site with Mr. John Robins, of Tavistock, in 1989 I found it to some extent unchanged since my visit nearly forty years earlier. The engine and winch were still there, the latter bearing the name "R. Wayland & Co., London S.E." while the single cylinder water-cooled engine, very rusted up and with smaller components missing, and which probably ran on paraffin, had twin 2'7" dia. flywheels on a 2¼" crankshaft with a broad 15" dia. pulley keyed to one extremity, but its purpose was unclear — possibly to drive some sort of rock-breaker or sizing device. The rim of a second broad pulley was lying near the winch but it seemed unlikely that there was any connection between the two.

A narrow trench up to 5 feet deep led N.W. from an excavation into loose rock and gravel and it is probable that its line formerly continued as the raised launder which I remember from my 1951 visit. The hut must have disappeared many years ago, while there was little trace of the dressing area beyond some overgrown parallel trenches which may once have been settling pits or strips.

To add a little further information, R.W. Toll, writing in 1951 about the neighbouring mineral deposits on Standon Hill at Baggator, (Ch. 16) which were a mile N.E. of Wapsworthy and being worked in 1925, said that in addition to tin these yielded ilmenite and zircon, also the more unusual mineral monazite, a compound containing the rare elements cerium, lanthanum, neodymium, praseodymium and thorium.

For anyone who enjoys a walk over rough ground I would say that the site is still worth a visit, but if my own experience there and elsewhere on the moor is anything to go by one needs both sharp eyes and a certain amount of luck to pick up even a piece of tin ore, let alone any of the more exotic minerals mentioned above. The prospect can be reached by approaching the hamlet of Wapsworthy by the road leading to it from the west and taking the first turning right, which leads to a footpath trending east. Follow the path until reaching the tributary, cross the latter and walk up the northeastern bank until the site is reached.

Very recently, and after the above account had been written, I learnt that Jack Cloke had had a son who had worked with him at Gawton and who would almost certainly have had some knowledge of the Wapsworthy venture. But sadly on trying to contact him I was told that he had died only a few months previously.

CHAPTER 2

LAST YEARS AT GOLDEN DAGGER MINE, POSTBRIDGE 685799

I HAVE WRITTEN THE NOTES IN THIS CHAPTER TO augment, to a limited extent, the details in Dr T.A.P. Greeves' book *Tin Mines and Miners of Dartmoor* (Devon Books 1986) but they can be read on their own; in writing them I have put particular emphasis on the period after 1924. Much information was kindly supplied to me by Mr Donald Smith, who was the mine manager in the late 1920s and I have supplemented this from my own recollections of over fifty years ago and from the notes I made following recent visits to the site. I am also indebted to Mr Justin Brooke, of Marazion, and to Mrs Beatrice Brook, formerly of Postbridge, for some further details.

Golden Dagger Mine is situated in the north-south valley of the Redwater Brook, half a mile south of the better known Birch Tor & Vitifer mining complex, and about a mile south east of the Warren Inn, Postbridge. Tin ore has been recovered intermittently from the alluvial deposits of the valley floor from time immemorial, while the parent veins or lodes from which most of the alluvial material was derived have been exploited in rather more recent years, both by opencast and by underground mining. Ramifications of these lodes cross the vicinity from east to west and their courses can be deduced today from the enormous trenches or gullies which the old miners dug in order to get at them, though the lodes themselves were quite narrow, filling near-vertical fissures in the ground only a foot or two wide, if that. This opencast mining ceased many years ago, while the last serious underground mining ended in 1914. Recovery of tin ore from the alluvium continued until about 1939 and the material extracted in latter years would of course have included some incompletely processed waste washed down from earlier workings.

It is not known how the mine came to be given its unusual, even romantic, name but although part of a prehistoric dagger decorated with gold is said to have been found nearby in 1872 the name Golden Dagger is thought to have been in use long before that date. Regarding gold, it is interesting to note that the occurrence of this metal in minute quantities on Dartmoor is not unknown, and it was reported that in 1878 the then manager of Golden Dagger found the remains of primitive gold-washing equipment on the mine.

Over the years, the mines of the Redwater Valley have been worked by a succession of companies or "adventurers", not always particularly successfully, one of the last such companies having been Dartmoor Tin

Plate II. Old Cornish stamps and waterwheel at Golden Dagger Mine last used c1914 and photographed in 1937.

Mines Ltd., which began work in 1923, spent a considerable amount of money on machinery and plant but seemingly ceased operations at Golden Dagger soon afterwards. Then early in 1925 a new company, Torr Trust, commenced operations, employing Donald Smith initially as engineer and then promoting him to manager. We are indebted to Mr Smith not only for the information he has provided but also for the large number of photographs he took covering the period from 1925 until work was suspended in 1930 many of which are reproduced in Dr Greeves' book.

During these last years much of the work of the mine was centred in and around the Engine House (Grid Ref. 685799) and the sketch plan shows its approximate layout. The large gas engine and gas producing plant were already in situ when Torr Trust took over, having been installed by Dartmoor Tin Mines, but neither was in fact used by Torr Trust who instead put in a smaller engine, a Petter semi-diesel.

In those days separation of the relatively heavy tin ore from the lighter waste and sand accompanying it was achieved mainly by the action of running water washing the material down a gently sloping surface, the valuable heavy grains settling near the top of the slope while the lighter waste was carried further down. At Golden Dagger there was an added complication in that the tin ore occurred intimately mixed with iron ore - another heavy mineral - making it difficult to achieve efficient separation by water alone; but fortunately this iron ore (specular

Plate III. The Engine House, Golden Dagger Mine looking north in 1987, with sites of Petter engine (centre), its cooling tanks (extreme left), gas engine (extreme right) and gas producing plant (centre distance).

Plate IV. Circular buddle near Engine House, Golden Dagger Mine, in 1989. When in use there would have been a wooden frame over it supporting a vertical spindle carrying the revolving sweeps.

haematite) is slightly magnetic so could be removed by a magnetic separator which had originally been installed at the neighbouring Vitifer Mine by Dartmoor Tin Mines.

In mining undertakings of this nature a good supply of water was always needed for processing or dressing the ore, and in the period immediately following the 1925 re-opening water was obtained from a spring located in a gulley east of the Engine House, which yielded just enough for this purpose. Smith, who took over as manager soon afterwards, was not satisfied with this arrangement and took steps to put matters on a better footing, firstly by cutting a ¼ mile extension to a leat formerly supplying old dressing floors at Grid Ref. 684803 which had been used in an earlier working and which in turn took its water from the Redwater Brook at Ref. 684805, and secondly by installing a water turbine and generator in the Engine House, so that the Petter engine only had to be used in dry weather, when there was insufficient water from the new leat extension to run the turbine. He also refurbished the magnetic separator, which by that time had been moved to Golden Dagger from Vitifer.

The cutting of the leat was a considerable task, necessitating the use of explosives and here the experience of Freddy Warne (of the Postbridge mining family of that name) was invaluable. The turbine and generator also came from Vitifer, ruins of whose turbine house can be seen at the bottom left hand corner of the photograph on page 15 of Atkinson, Burt and Waite's book *Dartmoor Mines*. Unfortunately, most of the original supply pipe was too rusted to be re-usable so Smith improvised the upper (low pressure) part with Colas drums, while a new angled (high pressure) section to connect to the turbine was specially made by F. Braby & Co. of Bristol. As Smith himself remarked, the transfer of turbine and generator from Vitifer to Golden Dagger was a considerable achievement for a 21-year old, and he added that one of the finest moments of his life was when, after opening the inlet valve for the first time, he watched the needle of the meter move up to 240 volts.

A point which had previously puzzled me was that as the shaft of the turbine was aligned north-south and that of the Petter engine east-west one wondered how the generator could have been positioned so that it could be driven by either power source. The explanation is that in winter it was driven by the turbine via a flanged coupling, then with the onset of drier weather it was uncoupled from the turbine and moved to an alternative position where it was driven by the Petter via a belt. The move was accomplished by reeving a taut wire diagonally across the Engine House, lifting the generator by block and tackle and sliding it across to the summer position.

Being a semi-diesel, the Petter had a hot bulb or hot dome on the cylinder head which had to be heated initially by a blowlamp, and being too heavy to crank, it had to be started by compressed air. If the air in its air bottle ran out before a start had been achieved the bottle had to be refilled by means of a hand pump - laborious, but Smith said it got you warm on a cold morning.

In the 1925-1930 working no crushing of the alluvial material was done - it was merely sized in a trommel, which was a large hollow iron cylinder pierced with holes of graduated sizes and revolving about a near-horizontal axis. Freshly dug material was fed into the upper end of the cylinder and emerged from the holes according to size of particles. Only the finer stuff from the trommel was retained for further treatment; Smith did contemplate installing a ball mill (a revolving cylindrical or conical casing containing cast iron balls which pulverised the material fed into it) in order to reduce the size of the larger fragments but the closure of the mine came before this could be done. While the mobile trommels featured in Dr Greeves' Plates 51 and 52 were originally driven by 3-HP electric motors, the motors were later replaced by small waterwheels mounted direct onto the ends of the 2" shafts carrying the cylinders or screens.

The fine material from a trommel was next treated in a circular buddle, which was a shallow cement (or sometimes wooden) cone, its surface sloping down towards its circumference. Ore was washed along a narrow channel or launder onto the top of the cone, from which it flowed outwards, the heaviest particles settling nearest the centre and the lighter waste lower down the slope. Slowly revolving sweeps brushed the surface of the deposit to keep it even and to prevent channels forming.

The best material from the circular buddles then went to a square buddle which was a simple inclined plane and finally to the chimming kieves. The kieves were open tubs in which the mixture of ore and water, still containing a small amount of waste sand, was stirred and allowed to settle - the waste at the top where it could be skimmed off. Settlement was aided by the knocker heads which were mechanical hammers operating on the trip-hammer principle, positioned so that the hammer heads struck the metal bands of the kieves which gave a more resonant blow than if they struck the wooden staves and also reduced wear and tear on the kieves themselves. They were operated by a small waterwheel sited behind the southern end of the Engine House and the sweeps of the circular buddles were worked by similar small wheels. Water for the wheels and for general dressing purposes was taken from the new leat via some of the 3½" steel pipes left behind by Dartmoor Tin Mines.

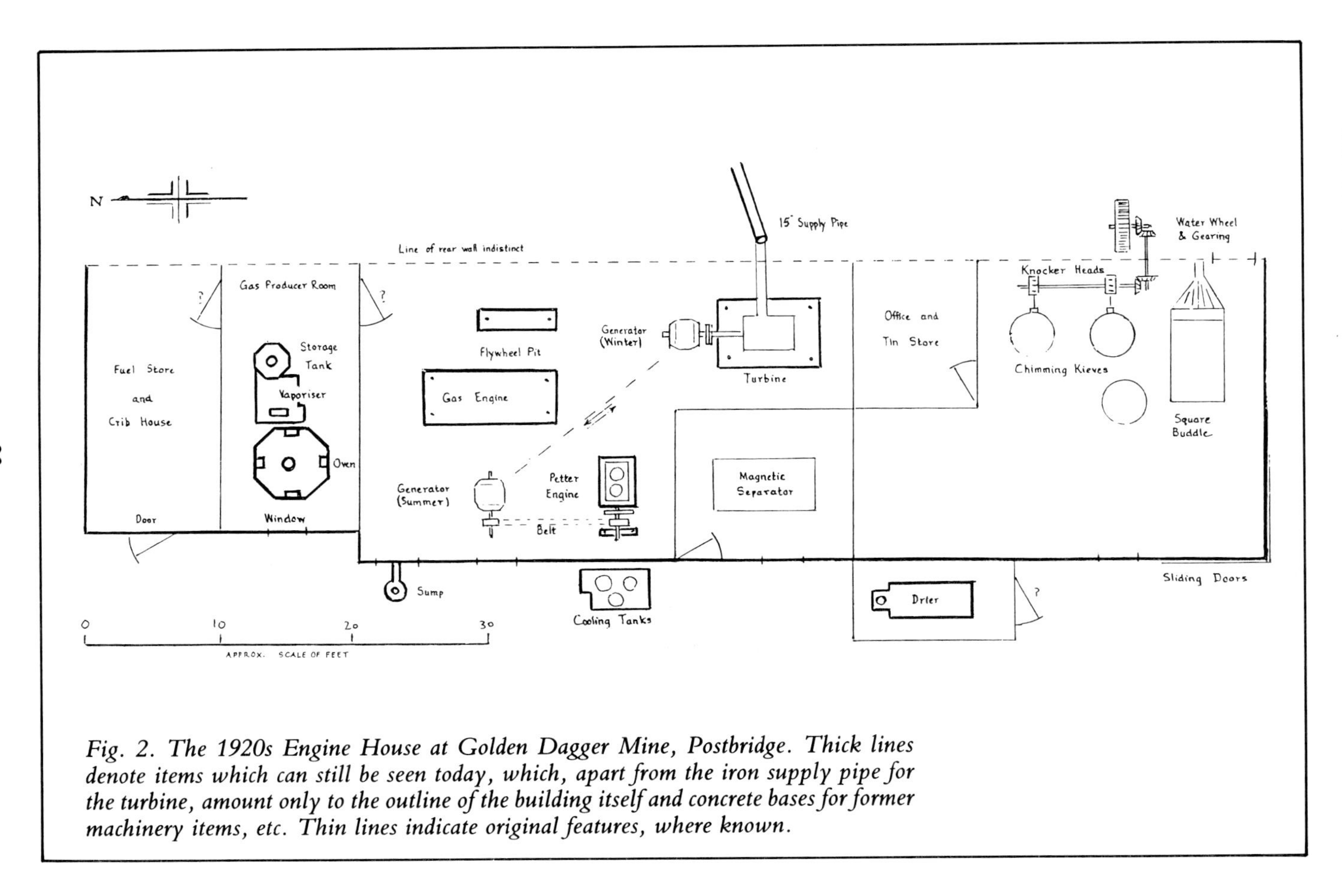

Fig. 2. The 1920s Engine House at Golden Dagger Mine, Postbridge. Thick lines denote items which can still be seen today, which, apart from the iron supply pipe for the turbine, amount only to the outline of the building itself and concrete bases for former machinery items, etc. Thin lines indicate original features, where known.

The concentrates which had undergone their final chimming still contained a considerable amount of specular iron which had to be removed in the magnetic separator prior to sale but before going to the separator they had to be dried. This was done in a small furnace consisting of a shallow iron tray with a fire under it whose flue was led up a brick stack surmounted by a round 6" chimney pot. The furnace was sited in an extension to the Engine House (see plan) which can be readily identified in Dr Greeves' Plate 56, the chimney being just discernible at the left hand (north) end of the extension. The cooling tanks of the Petter can also be seen in the same picture.

The magnetic separator consisted basically of a powerful electro-magnet with poles pointing downwards directly under which were two broad endless horizontal belts, one above the other and at right angles to each other, each moving slowly between pairs of pulleys. Before going to the separator the dried concentrate needed to be both cool and uncaked, so that the grains would run freely, otherwise tin particles could be lifted with the iron and lost. It was therefore sifted thinly onto the lower belt by means of a hopper and screen and on being carried beneath the magnet on the moving belt the specular iron was lifted and held against the underside of the upper (cross) belt and it dropped off into a box when it passed beyond the influence of the magnet, while the tin remained on the lower belt and fell into a second box when it passed over the pulley towards which it was travelling.

The speed of the belts and adjustment of the magnets were critical if a proper separation was to be obtained and the specular iron removed by the separator was checked frequently with a vanning shovel to make sure that no tin was being removed with it - recent examination of a sample from the specular iron waste heap near the Engine House showed no sign of containing anything but specular iron. In practice, separators were usually more complicated than as just described but the above details should give a general idea of how they worked.

After lying idle for some seven years, an attempt was made to re-open the mine in about 1937 and my first visit there was made on 26th September of that year. For me this was an unusually important day as it was the first mine I had so far seen which had showed any signs of actual activity, but unfortunately my diary entries were sketchy and imprecise. I noted that the dressing plant appeared to be functional (but being a Sunday there was no-one about), that there were "several small waterwheels" and that "overhead electric cables ran in various directions". I have no mental pictures at all of the appearance of either the Engine House or of the nearby dwelling known as Dinah's House (once occupied by the mine manager) though I must obviously have seen both and my photograph reproduced as Dr. Greeves' Plate 73 actually shows the end wall of the former. This is the more surprising when one remembers that my visit was made before today's depressing conifer forests had been planted, so that the whole area was still open moorland, making any buildings greatly more prominent than they would have been now.

I went out to the mine again about a year later, when I was able to meet Olver, the new manager. He must have taken me into the Engine House because I remember seeing the turbine and generator running, and recall his saying that apart from the cost of a pound or so of grease each year they had free electricity. The magnetic separator was also there but looked dilapidated though it had an open box of "black tin" (actually reddish brown) under it, from which I took a small sample and was later able to reduce it to metallic tin.

I did not see the mine again for nearly fifty years, my next visit being in 1987, by which date everything had changed beyond recognition. However, the outline of the Engine House was still easily traceable, also the turbine pit, 15" supply pipe, remains of drying furnace, and the concrete loadings for producer gas plant, gas engine and for the Petter engine and its cooling tanks, while the leat and headbox could be seen on the hillside to the east and the bases of a couple of concrete circular buddles to the south and south west.

I was curious to know, among other things, how the turbine and generator, left behind following the 1930 suspension of work (when most other plant was disposed of) came to be still serviceable in 1937 after seven years on a derelict site. I thought at first that they might have been kept in use to supply electricity to those houses in the valley which were still occupied in the 1930s, though a competent person would have been needed to operate and maintain them, and in the "dry season" there would have been little electricity in the absence of the Petter engine.

However, some further information has recently come to light which suggests that this was not the case: when the generating set was still at Vitifer electricity *was* also supplied to at least some of the nearby dwelling houses although its prime purpose was to supply the mine, but when moved to Golden Dagger only that mine was supplied. I am told that Dinah's House (only yards from the Golden Dagger Engine House) never had electricity although continuing to be occupied until the early 1940s.

In the intervening period 1930-37 it is now understood that Harry Warne (nicknamed "Silvertop") who, with his family, lived variously in one or other of the houses in the valley at that time, seemingly acted as caretaker, so would have kept an eye on things and perhaps even run the generator occasionally. This may have been an honorary post (unpaid?) but along with many miners and prospectors he was probably an optimist and have perhaps felt that he was doing something which might aid a subsequent re-opening of the mine.

While it is known that Torr Trust stopped production because of a drastic fall in the price of tin following the 1929 slump, beyond the fact that Olver went away to the war and was killed. I do not know how the final closure (in 1939 or 1940?) came about, nor do I know the name of the company he represented. But it is understood that the site was looked at again in about 1941, presumably by the Ministry of Supply, though nothing was done then nor, I imagine, at any time since.

The above notes still leave some unresolved queries and inconsistencies but even at this late stage it is not impossible that answers might be found to some of them. Although today's remains on the site are scanty I would say that the place is still worth a visit, which might bring to light traces of other features mentioned in *Tin Mines and Miners of Dartmoor.*

CHAPTER 3

HENSROOST TIN MINE, HEXWORTHY
655708

HENSROOST, OR HEXWORTHY, TIN MINE, SITUATED 4½ miles E.S.E. of Princetown, or a mile south of the Forest Inn, Hexworthy, presents an interesting study for the mining enthusiast. Located on open moorland within the Dartmoor National Park there are no difficulties over access and the clear ground contrasts well with the tangle of brambles and undergrowth which so often surrounds the valley mines; and being a mile from the nearest road an atmosphere of solitude prevails.

Fig. 3. Hensroost Tin Mine, Hexworthy. General surface plan.

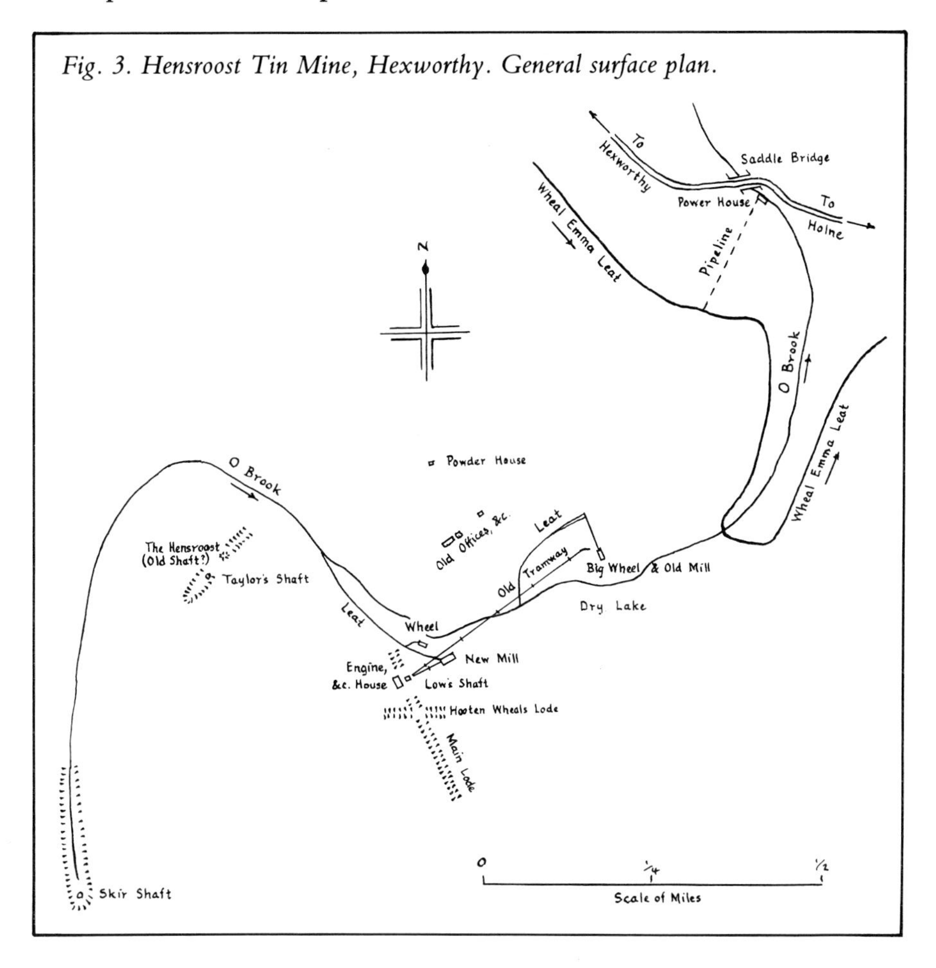

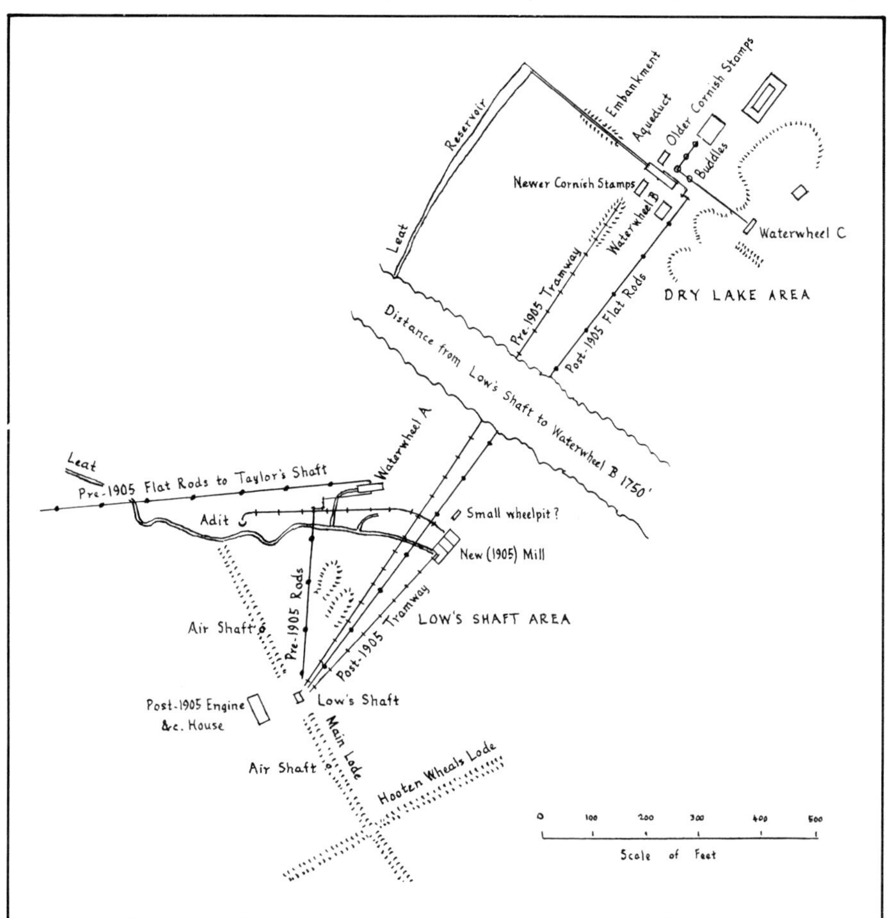

Fig. 4. Hensroost Tin Mine, Hexworthy. Detailed surface plan covering both the pre-1905 and the post-1905 workings.

At first glance the area may appear rather dull, but closer scrutiny quickly reveals traces of all the usual mining features of shafts, adits, spoil heaps, leats, aqueducts, waterwheel pits, flat rods, tramroads, dressing floors, buildings, etc, these being the more interesting in that they relate to three distinct epochs, namely the largely open-cast workings of the ancients, traditional 19th century mining and finally more or less modern 20th century activity.

The accompanying sketch plans show some of the more salient features, the oldest of which appear to be the open gullies (which should not be confused with later flat rod trenches) in the sector from south round to N.W. of Low's Shaft, possibly including Skir Shaft; there was also at least one old adit on Down Ridge, to the north of Low's.

In the latter part of the 19th century the mine was worked from Low's and Taylor's shafts, which were drained by Cornish beam pumps operated by waterwheel "A" by means of flat rods, the run of rods from this wheel to Taylor's being nearly 2,000 feet long. The dressing floors, where the ore was treated, were then situated at Dry Lake, where there was a battery of Cornish stamps for crushing the ore, powered by waterwheel "B". The latter was fed by a leat running N.E. from the O Brook, the lower part of which was widened to form a reservoir before turning S.E. along an embankment from which it was carried to the top of the wheel on a wooden aqueduct. The first set of stamps was probably erected soon after the middle of the 19th century and was on the N.E. side of the wheel but these were subsequently replaced by a newer set on the S.W. side, while further treatment of the crushed ore was carried out in four or more circular buddles worked by waterwheel "C". It is hard to visualise today that the hummocky and heather-covered ground adjoining waterwheels "B" and "C" was once the ore-dressing area and that it was, in part at least, covered in. In high summer it could be excessively hot there and Dr Greeves records a remark said to have been made by the tin-dresser to one of his assistants in about 1900: "Us be stiffled doun yurr!" For me those simple words spoken nearly a century ago somehow bring the scene to life.

Ore was brought to the stamps by cart in earlier days but later a tramroad was laid from Low's Shaft to Dry Lake. Just N.E. of Low's Shaft the ground sloped down fairly steeply and that portion of the tramroad took the form of a self-acting incline, full wagons going down pulling empty ones up, a common arrangement being for an incline to be single-track with a passing place in the middle. After reaching level ground at the foot of the incline the wagons are understood to have been pushed on to Dry Lake by hand, though it is possible that ponies may also have been used.

In about 1905 the mine was modernised, and in line with the "electric boom" of that period all plant except the pump which drained the workings was thence forward electrically driven by power from a hydro-electric station built at Saddle Bridge, a mile S.E. of Hexworthy and directly beside the road. The dressing floors at Dry Lake were abandoned in favour of an entirely new mill built just N.E. of Low's Shaft, but waterwheel "B" at Dry Lake was kept in use, this time to work the Cornish beam pump at Low's Shaft by means of another long run of flat rods - possibly the same ones which formerly served Taylor's Shaft, the latter having been by then abandoned.

For those interested in technicalities, the power station contained a 500 volt 110 Kw D.C. generator driven by a 6-foot diameter Pelton wheel taking its supply from the old Wheal Emma leat via a 16" diameter

Plate V. The big waterwheel at Dry Lake, Hensroost Mine, in about 1905. In distance, on left, former offices etc. Near left flat rod leading to Low's Shaft. Beyond wheel newer Cornish stamps. On right older Cornish stamps. (Print given by Dr. T.A.P. Greeves. Photographer not known).

rivetted iron pipe, with a fall of 183 feet, the current generated being taken to the mill area by overhead cables. Those who remember it have told me that, when running, the power house was an exceedingly noisy place. The man who looked after it - Harold Simmons from Scorriton - would play a small joke on visiting children when they went near the generator by throwing a spanner to one of them, but before the child could catch it, it would be whisked aside by the magnetic field of the generator coils.

Low's Shaft, measuring 12 feet by 6 feet to accommodate a double skip road, was 36 fathoms deep, with levels at 11 fms (drainage adit), 24 fms and 35 fms, and the electric hoist was of the Lidgerwood double-drum variety.

Rough ore from the shaft, containing of course a large proportion of waste rock, was fed to a 10-head battery of Californian stamps after the size of the larger pieces had been reduced in a rock-breaker. Working the stamps took some two-thirds of the available electricity and the management had so placed them that a further 10 heads could be added later should output justify it, but such a step would presumably have produced difficulties over power.

Plate VI. Electric winding gear at Low's Shaft, Hensroost Mine, in 1934, showing controller (left), braking levers, etc., (centre) and motor and double drum (right).

Plate VII. View down Low's Shaft, Hensroost Mine, in 1934. The debris includes a kibble, parts of the ladder-way and possible section of the wrought iron pump rod. The pump itself was probably never removed from the bottom of the shaft.

Pulped ore from the stamps was washed down in launders to three classifiers for sizing, thence to two Wilfley tables and a revolving slime table, after which it was passed over two circular buddles and a square buddle before being finally settled in kieves.

At the same time as the mill was put up a substantial two-storey building some 75 feet long was erected immediately S.W. of Low's Shaft. The ground floor included rooms for offices, the electric hoist, a blacksmith's shop and a "dry" (i.e. miners' changing room) while the upper floor was devoted to accommodation for miners unable to go home each day. For those who could get home it must have been a desolate journey in winter, particularly in the dark, and I remember being told that in one local household all candle ends had to be saved for father who used to try and see his way to the mine by means of a lighted candle-end in a jam jar.

A small "powder house" was built some 600 yards N.N.E. of Low's Shaft and an elaborate safety procedure was enforced in respect of the handling of explosives (latterly dynamite) including double doors to the house, use of copper tools only and wearing of soft over-shoes by men involved.

The more recent periods of work were 1852-55, 1889-1903, 1905-12 and 1915-16. A further attempt to work the mine was made in 1919

Plate VIII. Looking north from Low's Shaft, Hensroost Mine, in 1938 with fallen headgear (near left), pump beam (near right) and gantry to mill (middle distance).

Plate IX. Site of new mill, Hensroost Mine, in 1976. In foreground are two circular buddles and the remains of the armature of the stamps motor.

employing men back from the War but (a report stated) “three months’ experience showed them to be of little use, most of their time being devoted to ‘the bottle’ so they were accordingly discharged”. After that the mine was put into care and maintenance for a time, with only the pump kept going to prevent the underground workings from being inundated. Then in 1920 a storm of exceptional severity destroyed the aqueduct taking water to the pumping wheel at Dry Lake, which stopped the pump allowing the workings to flood and, according to a contemporary report, causing the collar of Low’s Shaft to collapse, effectively putting paid to the whole concern, though an agent (Dudley le Ros) remained in nominal charge until about 1925. Regarding the collapse of the collar, however, with adit level 11 fathoms below surface and the shaft sunk in granite, it is hard to see a connection between the flooding and the collapse and one wonders “did it fall or was it pushed?” An open shaft could have been a menace which local graziers and others could have regarded with disfavour. By the same token the stone buildings in the vicinity which are now mere rubble heaps did not deteriorate naturally — they were destroyed by American artillery practising for the D-Day landings in 1944.

During the late 19th and early 20th centuries the undertaking was run by a succession of adventurers: Hexworthy Tin Mining Co., Dartmoor Minerals Ltd., Golden Dagger Co., Standard Mica & Exploration Co. and others but was never particularly successful.

I first saw the mine in 1927, when the power house at Saddle Bridge was seemingly in a serviceable state, with the Pelton wheel at the N.W. end connected to the generator at the S.E. end by a belt, with meters and switchgear against the S.E. wall, while overhead cables led up the hillside towards the mill. Later recollections are that each electricity post had two crossbars, one large and one small, the larger carrying the power cables while one might guess that the smaller ones carried a telephone line between the hoist, mill and power house, but this is surmise.

The mill building and its contents were also in good order in those earlier years, with a tramroad from Low's Shaft carried on a gantry to the stamps, which were on one side of the top level in the mill (leaving space for a further set), tables were on the intermediate level and buddles and kieves on the lowest level. In the southernmost corner of the mill a recess was utilised as a store with rough shelving on which were nuts, bolts and other small items.

The large building immediately S.W. of Low's Shaft was roofless and generally ruinous in the early 1930s, but the electric hoist was still there, though obviously unserviceable. At the shaft, the headgear had fallen and the shaft itself was in much the same state as it is today, i.e. with sides run in. The rocker beam of the pump was still in place with the wrought iron pump rod leading down the shaft, while at Dry Lake the Cornish stamps had been removed but the big waterwheel (though lacking its launder) was fairly intact. In a diary entry of August, 1934, I noted that "the connection between it and the (rocker beam of the) pump is by a reciprocating iron rod which is raised three feet above the ground on pulley wheels placed every few yards". The rod was of wrought iron and about two inches in diameter.

The power house was stripped out in 1929, the big wheel was dismantled in 1935 and the mill building with most of its contents had gone by 1938.

Today, while only vestiges of the various buildings remain, many other features mentioned above can still be traced, even including a certain amount of ironmongery, e.g. the armature of the electric motor which drove the stamps, some of the iron pulleys which carried the flat rods, odd rails and metal sleepers of tramroads, a heap of stones representing the powder house, ringbolts for the guy wires of the launder carrying water to the big wheel at Dry Lake and fragments of the 16" pipe taking water to the power house at Saddle Bridge. These are, however, a scant memorial to a venture which, while it could never be described as great, was nevertheless an interesting one and in many ways well conceived, although without doubt far more money was put into the mine than ever came out of it. Perhaps we should call to mind the old Dartmoor adage, referring to attempts to industrialise the heart of the moor, "Scratch my back and you'll pay for it".

Plate IXa. Sketch of Hensroost Mine made in about 1935 showing (left to right) Powder House, Offices etc., (later used as a house for the Managers), the 1905 Mill and gantry and the 1905 Engine House, etc.

CHAPTER 4

THE MARYTAVY MINES

1. Wheal Friendship 506794

OF THE DEVON MINES, WHEAL FRIENDSHIP WAS second in magnitude only to Devon Great Consols and had a considerably longer life than the latter, having worked almost continuously from the late 1700s until 1925. Up to the 1870s operations were usually very profitable but in subsequent years less so.

As at Devon Great Consols the principal mineral worked, until the 1870s, was copper and as copper production diminished after that so the management began to pay attention to arsenic, building the enormous condensing chambers and flues whose ruins still form a major feature of the Marytavy landscape today. Unlike Devon Great Consols, however, a certain amount of tin was also produced in these later years.

In earlier days the parts of the mine most actively worked were in the vicinity of the main Tavistock to Okehampton road at Marytavy, extending eastwards to rather beyond the Cholwell Brook; these were the deepest workings. As copper production gave way to tin and arsenic the area further to the east was developed, though only to a limited depth, the principal shaft in this eastern section, sunk in the early 1880s, being known as Bennett's.

Much has been written about the earlier history of mine — in fact few books on Devon mining fail to mention it — and I will not seek to reproduce such information. I propose instead to concentrate on the more recent, and less documented, years of the mine's life, supplementing the available data from my own recollections dating from the early 1930s.

Wheal Friendship has always been noted for its extensive use of water power, the water being conducted to the mine in two principal leats, both supplied from the Tavy. One had its intake at Tavy Cleave, serving first Wheal Jewell and then Wheal Betsy before descending to Wheal Friendship via the Cholwell Brook. The other had its take-off at Hill Bridge and older maps show it flowing along a contour to a point 3/8 mile S.W. of Horndon, where it apparently ended abruptly, but in fact it entered a tunnel through which it flowed northwestwards for some 1/4 mile, emerging near Axna. The course of the tunnel is marked on older maps by nearly a dozen "old shafts", suggesting that to expedite completion there may have been simultaneous drives in both directions from each shaft linking up with the drives from adjacent shafts. From Axna it went across fields to the large wheelpit just S.W. of Brenton's

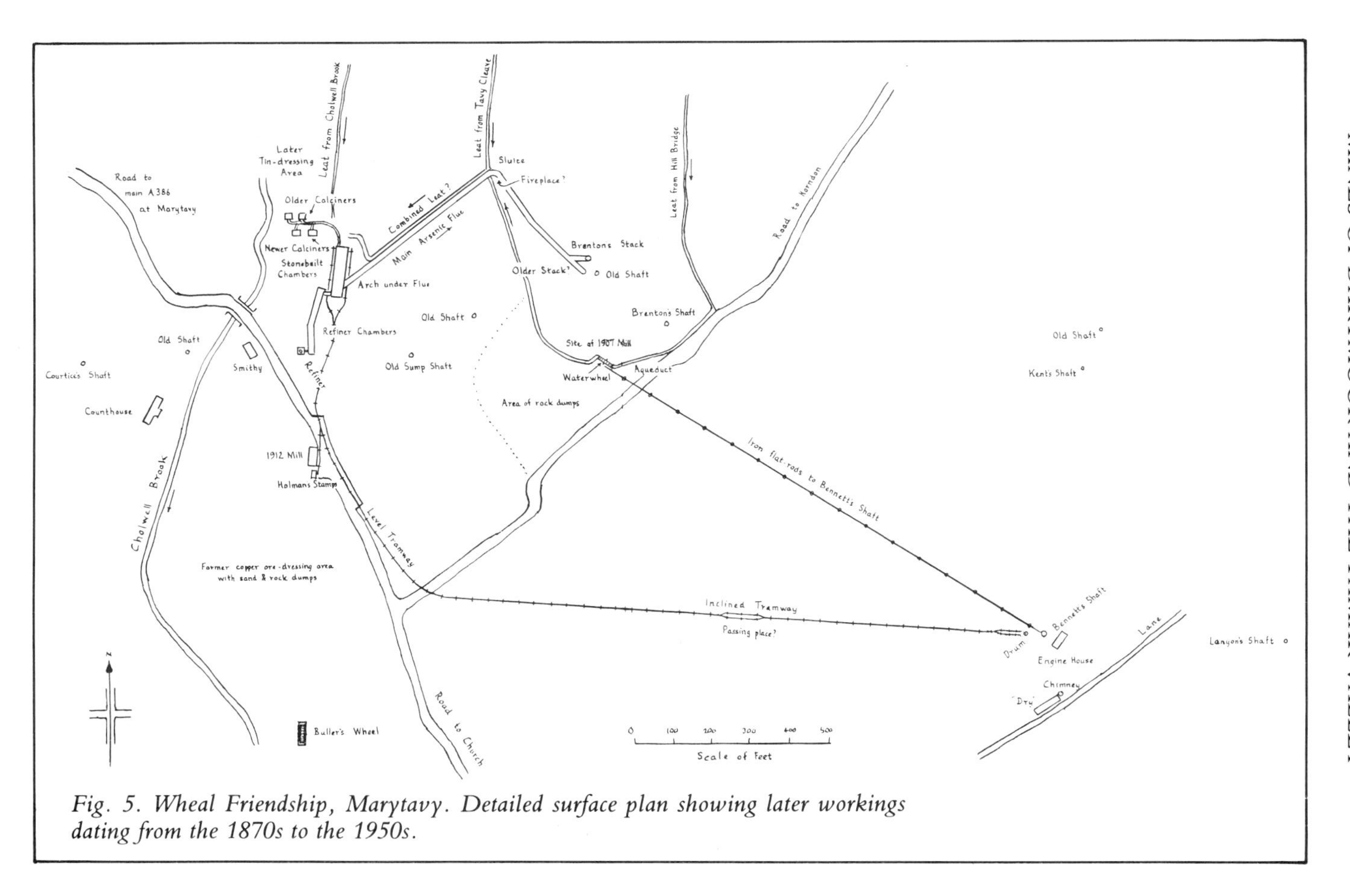

Fig. 5. Wheal Friendship, Marytavy. Detailed surface plan showing later workings dating from the 1870s to the 1950s.

Shaft, afterwards joining the other leat at the angle of the main arsenic flue, the combined flow of the two very probably going down beside the flue to the lower parts of the mine, but this is conjecture.

Up until the end of the 19th century water from the leats was used, by ingenious means, to turn a succession of waterwheels ending with the huge Buller's Wheel which was 50 feet in diameter by 10 feet breast and situated 100 yards S.W. of Marytavy School. But at the end of the century these arrangements were deemed antiquated and it was recommended that they should be replaced by an electric generating plant driven by a modern turbine. A 200 HP water turbine was in fact eventually installed, but not until many years later and even so one imagines that the use of electricity was only limited.

Returning to the general history of the mine, it is likely that the original ranges of stonebuilt calciners, condensing chambers and flues were built in the 1870s concurrently with the running down of copper production. These were constructed on the same heroic scale which doubtless pertained at Devon Great Consols in those days — the latter's 1870s arsenic works was of course totally destroyed soon after the abandonment in 1903 — and there were probably two original calciners of unknown design, two newer Brunton-type ones being added at a much later date. Flues from all four were connected to the same main flue leading to two separate ranges of arsenic condensing chambers with eight chambers each for condensing crude arsenic (the size of an individual chamber was 10 feet by 5½ feet by 9 feet high) while the flue up to the base of the stack was over 800 feet long. It is possible that Brenton's Stack replaced an earlier and perhaps smaller stack which may not have proved tall enough to produce the necessary draught through such a long length of near-horizontal flues, but again this is conjecture on my part. But it is notable that Brenton's was at the end of a short branch flue near the top of the main flue so possibly the older stack (if there was one) had to be kept in use while Brenton's Stack was being built. It has also been reported that there was a supplementary furnace at the angle of the flue, where its direction changes from N.E. to S.E., presumably to augment the draught. Such a feature was not unusual and a similar fireplace can still be seen today at the bottom of the 1920s stack at Devon Great Consols.

In 1880, the name of the mine was changed from Wheal Friendship to Devon Friendship and it seems that Bennett's Shaft was sunk round about that time — it was certainly in use by 1882, pumping being achieved by means of quarter of a mile of iron flat rods worked by the wheel immediately S.W. of Brenton's Shaft. Both tin and arsenic ores were raised from Bennett's Shaft and were conveyed down to the original dressing area situated about ⅜ mile N.N.W. of Marytavy Church by

Plate X. Headgear of Bennett's Shaft, Wheal Friendship, in 1932.

means of an inclined tramway laid in the early 1880s but these operations were not successful, ceasing in 1885 allowing Bennett's Shaft to flood and recommencing in 1891, this time at Lanyon's Shaft. But during the ensuing few years there were managerial disagreements and work again ceased in 1900, re-starting in 1907 under a new owner who partly unwatered Bennett's Shaft and built a small treatment plant near Brenton's Shaft. Then in 1912 the property was taken over by Wheal Jewell & Marytavy Mines Ltd., who dismantled the mill at Brenton's and built an entirely fresh and more sophisticated one on the S.W. side of the road leading down to Marytavy Church, opposite the track to the calciners. This plant included a pair of Holman's pneumatic stamps on the site of an earlier battery of Cornish stamps, also tables, Frue vanners, etc., and was worked partly by waterwheels and partly by a 70 HP gas engine. Bennett's Shaft was again closed down and underground work concentrated at the nearby Wheal Jewell but work at the latter apparently lapsed in 1918, after which it was restricted to dump picking, which enabled the calciners to be kept in use; then in 1923 underground work was once again re-started from Bennett's Shaft. C.F. Barclay, who was involved with the mine between 1923 and 1925, said that the inclined tramroad to the new mill was re-laid at that time, two new Brunton calciners were built and the chambers and older calciners repaired. The 200 HP turbine was installed to drive the stamps and other plant though some waterwheels were retained and the 70 HP gas engine was kept in reserve against periods of drought. Although the earlier recommendation had been for a hydro-electric plant with the various items of machinery driven by individual motors I think it more likely that in the 1920s power for the mill was transmitted by means of overhead shafting and belts.

Plate XI. End of flat rod, with housing for bearing brasses, originally leading from waterwheel near Brenton's Shaft to Bennett's Shaft, Wheal Friendship, photographed in 1989.

Plate XII. One of the two boilers supplying steam to the winding engine at Bennett's Shaft, Wheal Friendship, photographed in 1932.

Plate XIII. Twin cylinder horizontal steam winding engine at Bennett's Shaft, Wheal Friendship, in 1932.

A query arises over the means for refining the crude arsenic collected in the old chambers. Though arsenic may have been sold in its crude state it seems likelier that an earlier refiner and refiner chambers existed but I have not been able to verify this. What is certain, however, is that a newer range of chambers, together with a refining furnace (the latter probably identical to that used at Devon Great Consols in the 1920s) was built to the south of the old stonebuilt chambers. The former can be seen clearly in the D.O.E. air photograph of 1949 which shows a single range of mostly roofless chambers, of which 20 can be counted, with the outline of a square building at the southern end with a circle within it representing the refiner itself. The other end of the chambers was connected into the main arsenic flue and although not evident from the photograph it is known that the connection was through a 3' 6" diameter rivetted iron pipe, the whole set-up being closely akin to that at Devon Great Consols. But despite these excellent arrangements the arsenic slump of 1925 forced a final cessation of any major activity on 31st July of that year.

Plate XIV. Winding engine at Bennett's Shaft, Wheal Friendship, in 1935, by which time the building housing it had been largely demolished although the machinery was intact. A steam line leading to the headgear can be seen on the left, beyond the flywheel of the engine.

Since then a little work has been done to recover dump material, initially for a short time in the early 1930s by R.W. Toll (formerly manager of Tavy Consols); then in about 1947 a lone prospector named Fieldhouse put up a small plant to treat tailings and was there for a couple of years but reportedly did not do very well out of it. Finally, in the 1950s, it is understood that some tailings were removed for treatment,

Plate XV. 70 H.P. gas engine at the post-1912 mill, Wheal Friendship, in 1935 (J.B.M. Adams).

Plate XVI. Arsenic condensing chambers at Wheal Friendship in 1963 when outer walls were still intact. In centre foreground is the 3'6" diameter metal flue leading up from the refiner chambers (F.L. Booker).

either in Cornwall or on the spot. On a visit in 1964 I noted that the roadside 1912 building contained three Wilfley tables and a flotation cell, assumed to date from the 1950s.

I first saw the mine in 1932 when Bennett's Shaft (500 yards N.E. of Marytavy Church) had a massive modern headgear with nearby engine house containing a two-cylinder steam winding engine and two boilers, each with a tall iron chimney. A calendar was hanging up near the engine with pages prior to July, 1925, torn off.

Primary crushing was evidently carried out in a rock-breaker placed in the lower part of the headgear above the ore bin and just visible in a photograph taken in 1935. The picture gives no direct clue as to how the rock-breaker was powered but another view shows an unmistakable steam line from one of the boilers to the bottom of the headgear, suggesting the possible presence of a steam engine there although this would have been somewhat unusual; if there was such an engine it could also have worked an air compressor for rock drills - these must have been used and I do not recall seeing a compressor in the engine house itself.

Unfortunately when I made my visits in 1932-1935 I was too young to know what features I should have been looking for and this also applies to pumping arrangements at Bennett's Shaft, of which I have no recollection whatsoever, except that in 1935 I noted that a pair of 4" iron pipes led up the side of the shaft to the surface. In this connection it may be mentioned that not only is the wheelpit near Brenton's Shaft exactly aligned on Bennett's Shaft but that the end section of the flat rods was still, in 1990, actually lying beside it, complete with the forged housing for the bearing brasses which had once fitted onto the crank of the waterwheel. The other end of the rod, which was 2" diameter, pointed in the direction of Bennett's Shaft but disappeared into a heap of rubble nearby. The rectangular collar of Bennett's Shaft (still just visible in 1990) had the customary two recesses, one aligned on the distant wheelpit and formerly accommodating the rocker bob and the other at right angles to it for the balance box. Though these features clearly date from earlier workings it is not wholly impossible that they were still employed in the 1920s, as an identical arrangement at Central and South Devon United Mines on the other side of the Tavy remained in use until 1922.

The inclined tramroad, with metals still in place in 1932, led down towards the dressing area between the road to the church and the Cholwell Brook. This incline had been gravity-operated, full trucks going down pulling empty ones up, controlled by a drum with braking gear at the upper end which I should have photographed but unfortunately did not. Incidentally this was not the "drum" marked on the 1907 6" Ordnance map, although this, too, was still in place in 1932, aligned on the tramway, but pertained to an earlier working.

In 1932 the original arsenic chambers appeared to be in reasonable condition, with a tramroad, with tramwagons still on it, running beside them on the eastern side. It is known that the tramroad divided, the other branch serving the chambers on the western side, but though I recall a set of points, presumably at that junction, I did not see the other branch nor do I know how it passed the 3'6" diameter flue leading up from the refiner chambers. I do, however, remember an arch where the eastern branch went under the flue leading up to Brenton's Stack. I did not see the calciners then though the newer Bruntons would almost certainly have been still intact: the 1949 air photograph shows them to be roofed and I do not believe they were stripped out until the 1950s. Nor did I see the refiner and refiner chambers at that time, and by the time I did see the chambers, which was in 1966, they were largely ruinous heaps of red brick, though it was possible to determine that each chamber had been 12 feet by 4 feet, while the refiner was a rubble heap of yellow bricks of which enough remained to indicate that it had been circular and 15 feet in diameter.

The pair of Holman's stamps was sited on the S.W. side of the road to the church and some 700 yards N.N.W. of the latter, which again I failed to photograph. In 1943 the building by the road and near the stamps (already mentioned as containing three Wilfley tables and a flotation cell in 1964) housed a concentrating table and three circular buddles, while on the level ground below the stamps were two tables,

Plate XVII. Arsenic condensing chambers (with outer wall now missing) at Wheal Friendship in 1989.

Plate XVIII. Individual condensing chamber (outer wall now missing) showing (left) arched opening communicating with next chamber, Wheal Friendship, 1989.

five Frue vanners and two waterwheels. I never sighted the turbine, while the gas engine, seen in the building beside the road in 1935, had gone by 1943. Most of the remaining items, albeit in a dilapidated state, were still there until at least the mid-1940s, and the stamps were still there in 1949. At Bennett's Shaft the engine house and contents had gone by 1943 and the headgear by 1949, the shaft itself being filled in some years later, probably in the early 1960s.

Brenton's Stack, at the upper end of the main flue, was destroyed by the Territorial Army as a demolition exercise in 1954. Judging by newspaper reports of the time this was a very inept performance, large rocks being hurled a quarter of a mile and more, damaging roofs of some houses and causing much indignation both on the part of local residents and of mine preservationists headed by A.K. Hamilton Jenkin. However, I must say in fairness that the stack had begun to deteriorate as far back as 1937 and that by 1947 the top third of it had fallen of its own accord.

In addition to features already mentioned, quite a lot of identifiable detail still remained in 1990, but the only surviving building (apart from the Counthouse — now a private dwelling) is one a few yards from Bennett's Shaft with a small conventional mine stack attached to it, which was the "dry". From Bennett's Shaft the course of the incline

Plate XIX. Remains of one of the two newer Brunton calciners at Wheal Friendship in 1989 showing (slightly to left of arch in centre) part of the brick well in which the circular furnace bed revolved.

down to the Horndon road is indicated by half a dozen field gates in a straight line, and the actual track bed can be discerned in places. After crossing the Horndon road the track followed a contour north westwards to the site of the Holman's stamps and the beginning of this contour course was disclosed by crop-marks in the drought of 1989.

The remains of the two newer calciners clearly show the latter to have been Bruntons and some of the sheet iron dampers used to control the flow of flue gases are still in place in grooved guides made from lengths of "bridge" type tramroad rails. Attempts to locate the auxiliary furnace at the angle of the main flue have been unsuccessful due to undergrowth and general debris.

Immediately north of the calciners was a small ore-dressing area in which at least one fairly modern circular buddle can be found in dense undergrowth, together with some other and as yet unidentified remains. Water is thought to have been brought to this area in a small leat taken from the Cholwell Brook ¼ mile further upstream and this may well have been the area in which Fieldhouse operated in the late 1940s, as I remember R.W. Toll saying that his plant was "behind the calciners."

The two principal leats, already referred to above, are still in use but now end at the Wheal Jewell and the Bennett's Shaft reservoirs respectively, from which the water is piped down to the present day hydro-electric station.

In the ore-dressing area round the site of the Holman's stamps regrettably almost nothing now remains. While I well remember the building housing the gas engine, etc., a recent search failed to find any trace of its exact position. I can only say that it was large, of corrugated iron on an angle iron frame and that one could walk straight into it from the road. It is probable that the heap of twisted and rusty angle iron lying on the rough ground nearby was originally part of the frame of this building.

Likewise though the Holman's stamps were still in place in 1949 and the masonry supporting them was there for some years after the stamps themselves had been removed, nothing now seems to remain. The whole area between the road and the brook has been so altered by the removal of material over the years and has become so overgrown in parts that I have found it impossible, even with the aid of photographs, to pinpoint the positions of the many interesting features which I remember from the thirties and forties.

Ownership of land on and around such a large site is inevitably complex but both Marytavy and Petertavy are well served by public footpaths.

2. Wheal Jewell 526813

Another very old mine, dating back to the end of the 18th century, represented by scattered workings on Kingsett Down, about 3/4 mile north of Horndon, the last major activity having been for tin and arsenic between 1912 and 1918, when the mine was worked in conjunction with Wheal Friendship. H.G. Dines, writing in 1956, said that some attention was again paid to the mine in 1924, but this could have only been short lived.

There were at least six shafts in the area between the road from Horndon to Willsworthy and the present day Wheal Jewell reservoir, of which only those known respectively as No. 3 and as North shafts were worked to any extent in the 1912-1918 period, while a small amount of development was carried out from No. 4. No. 3 went to 70 fathoms from surface, North shaft to 37, and No. 4 to about 6. Ore from these shafts went to a bin situated just E.S.E. of No. 3 from which it was transported to Wheal Friendship for treatment. There was also a shaft known as New or West Jewell shaft, (Grid Ref. 518813) but this is not thought to have been worked in recent years.

In this final period power was provided by a two-stage air compressor sited at Wheal Betsy on the west bank of the Cholwell Brook some 900 yards south of the surviving engine house at Job's Shaft and was worked

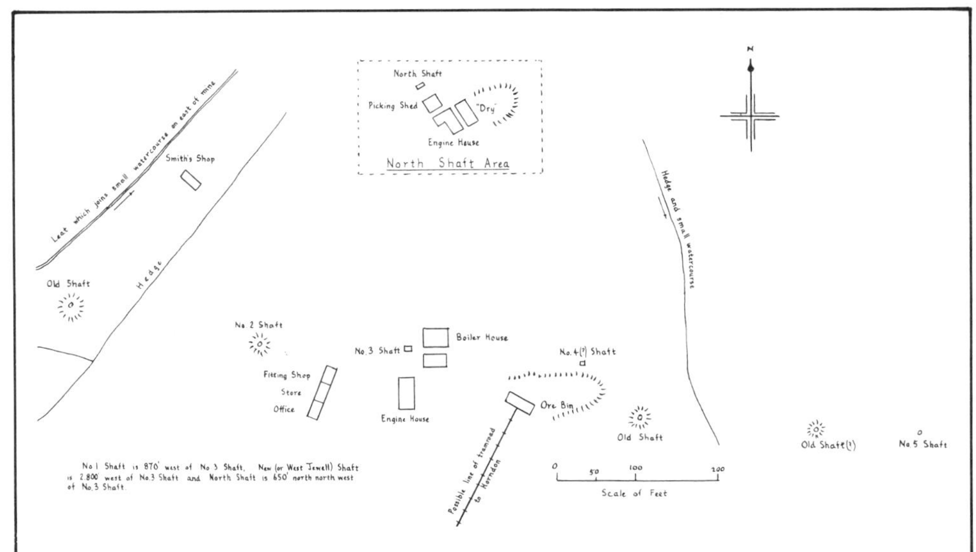

Fig. 6. Wheal Jewell, Marytavy. Surface plan covering activity between about 1912 and 1918.

by two Pelton wheels. Water for the wheels came from a new leat which took its supply from the old Wheal Friendship leat from Tavy Cleave at a point just west of today's Wheal Jewell reservoir and then ran parallel to, and just to the west of, the main Tavistock to Okehampton road to a headbox on the S.E. flank of Gibbet Hill, thence down a 20" pipeline to the compressor house. Compressed air at 90 p.s.i. was piped to the mine, over a mile away, through a 6" cast iron main, according to E. Terrell writing in 1914, where it was used to work pumping, winding and rock drilling machinery. A few years ago I spoke to an old ex-miner who had been at Wheal Jewell at that time and he told me that the power arrangements had worked well.

I saw the compressor in 1933, when it appeared to be in first rate condition, my recollections being that it looked like a small 5-cylinder vertical marine engine. The foundations of the building housing it can still be seen, as can the track of the 20" supply pipe from the leat ¼ mile to the west, but no trace of the air line to Wheal Jewell seems to have survived.

Likewise I saw the workings on Kingsett Down for the first time in 1933 when at least three shafts were open - one with fairly modern steel headgear, assumed to have been No. 3, one with primitive wooden tripod prospecting headgear, probably No. 4, and one an incline shaft with no headgear but with machinery shed nearby which was without doubt North shaft. The latter shaft was, I think, fitted with twin tramroads or skiproads, so apparently amounted to an inclined plane,

Plate XX. Embankment at end of presumed tramway to the loading stage near the Chapel at Horndon, in 1990. It has not been possible to photograph the loading stage itself as it is now obscured by trees and bushes.

thus doing away with the need for normal headgear. This inclined shaft was flooded to within about 30 feet of surface but it was possible to climb down to the water level without difficulty.

The headgears of the two shafts were still in place in the mid-1940s but had gone by 1950. At North shaft, as recently as 1969, sufficient of the timbering and of one skipway remained to enable the inclination of the shaft to be judged even though the shaft itself was almost full of rubbish but by 1984 these features were no longer visible. It may be mentioned that the rectangle of thin concrete on the S.E. side of the shaft was the floor of the "dry". The heavier concrete floor of the machinery shed, directly beside the dry, was broken up when the machinery was removed so that its site is now grassed over. New, or West Jewell, shaft is marked by a leat and wheelpit together with some dumps from which material appears to have been removed relatively recently.

As already stated, ore was sent to Wheal Friendship for treatment in the 1912-1918 working, very probably in a road trailer hauled by the steam traction engine whose rusting wreck was standing near Brenton's Stack in 1935. A similar arrangement for transport of ore existed at Devon Great Consols in the early 1920s, their traction engine having been known locally as Old Stinkpot.

It is possible that a tramway was laid from Wheal Jewell ore bin to a loading stage on the west side of the road to Willsworthy but this is supposition.

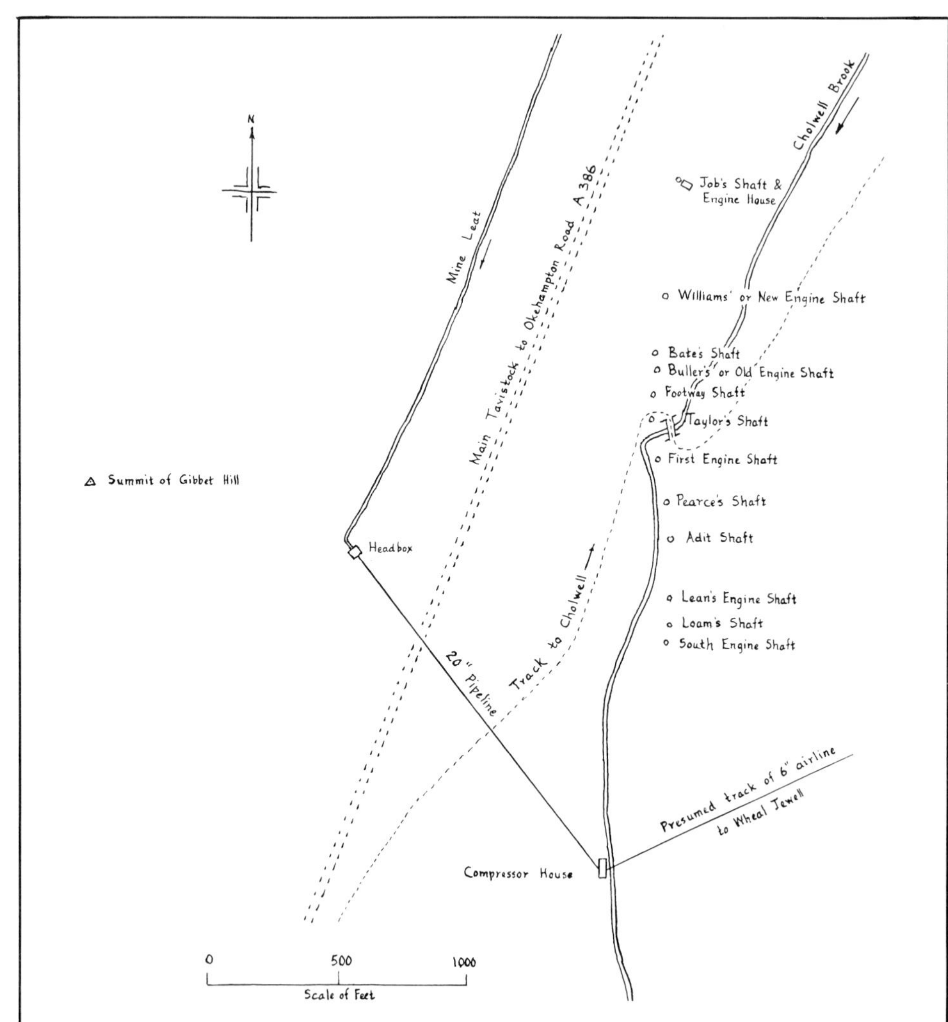

Fig. 7. Wheal Betsy, Marytavy. Surface plan showing shafts dating from the pre-1877 period, also features connected with the supply of compressed air to Wheal Jewell between about 1912 and 1918.

3. Wheal Betsy 510814

Any description of the Marytavy mining district would be incomplete without a reference to Wheal Betsy, even though that mine has not been actually worked in the post-1913 period. The site was nevertheless the scene of some activity between about 1912 and 1918 on account of the water-driven air-compressing plant built there to serve Wheal Jewell, as described in Section 2 above, while the engine house at Job's Shaft,

Plate XXI. Engine House at Job's Shaft, Wheal Betsy, in 1989.

beside the A.386 road, must be the finest surviving example of such a building in Devon.

Wheal Betsy is yet another very old mine, already in existence by the middle of the 18th century. In earlier days it was worked in conjunction with Wheal Friendship, for a time being known as North Wheal Friendship and at a later date as Prince Arthur Consols, and was finally abandoned in 1877. The mineral produced was silver-lead (lead ore containing a few ounces of silver to the ton), much of the ore being smelted on the mine.

There were about a dozen shafts, sunk along a ¾ mile stretch of a north-south lode in the deep valley of the Cholwell Brook immediately east of the main (A.386) road from Tavistock to Okehampton road a mile north of Marytavy. The lode formed part of the Great Crosscourse of Wheal Friendship, the total length of which is said to have been traced from Lydford to Horrabridge, a distance of eight miles, but not all of it was actually mineralised.

The deepest part of the mine was in the northern part of the sett in the vicinity of Job's Shaft, where an ultimate depth of 170 fathoms from surface was reached. The extent of the underground workings may be gauged from the extensive dumps of waste rock remaining today, amongst which lustrous specimens of lead ore (galena) may still be picked up occasionally.

Apart from the removal of the air-compressing plant mentioned above, this site, dominated by the Job's Shaft engine house, looks almost exactly as it did when I first saw it in 1932. However the engine house narrowly escaped destruction in 1954 when, only days after the blowing-up of Brenton's Stack (see Section 1 above), the Electricity Board gave the Army permission to demolish it. Fortunately, through the prompt intervention of Mr A.K. Hamilton Jenkin and others, this piece of vandalism was prevented and the building is now in the hands of the National Trust, who had it repaired and made safe in 1968 - an appropriate date as it was the centenary of the year in which the pumping engine was installed.

Beyond the fact that the long row of rough granite posts beside the main road near the engine house used to be known as Annie Pinkham's Men (I suppose she must have been friendly with the miners) the only other point of interest that comes to mind is that among the smaller dumps on the west side of the main road used to be an open shaft containing the remains of the vertical wooden pump rod, complete with massive metal strapping plates. This shaft was open in 1937 but has now been filled in.

Plate XXII. Old shaft with remains of pump rod on Gibbet Hill, near Wheal Betsy in 1937.

CHAPTER 5

DEVON UNITED MINES, PETERTAVY
522794 to 513786

WHILE MINING REMAINS IN WEST DEVON AND EAST Cornwall have become generally scarcer in recent years, at Devon United Mines, on the east bank of the Tavy, as well as at Wheal Friendship on the opposite side of the river, are still to be found an unusual number of identifiable features, possibly more at the former than at the latter. For this reason I am taking Devon United - in particular the Central and South mines - in considerable detail in an endeavour to reconcile present day remains with past activity.

Along a mile long stretch of the east bank of the Tavy immediately below Horndon Bridge are the three mines of Devon United - North Devon United (formerly known as East Wheal Friendship), Central Devon United (a relatively new mine, started soon after 1900) and South Devon United (formerly known as Wheal Ann and at one time worked with South Wheal Friendship on the other side of the river). In addition an adit known as Bennett's Adit was driven east from near the river at a point midway between the North and Central mines.

The North mine, formerly worked fairly extensively for copper, has been idle since the 1850s and its depth does not appear to be known; an adit was partly cleared in 1920 but as the lode on which it had been driven showed a poor mineral content this work was not pursued. Likewise Bennett's Adit, driven in 1918 on an eastward extension of the tin and arsenic Bennett's Lode of Wheal Friendship, proved unpromising and mining there was very limited. Today's surface remains do not amount to much at either of these locations and they will not be considered further in this chapter.

In contrast the Central and South mines were worked well into the 20th century, up to 40 men being employed latterly by the Contin Syndicate, and were not finally abandoned until 1922. At each mine was a well equipped shaft with a tramway joining the two locations and all treatment of ore was carried out at the South mine. Both tin and arsenic were mined, the South mine, some 50 fathoms deep, producing most of the tin and the Central mine, about half that depth, most of the arsenic. The underground workings of both mines are fully documented in H.G. Dines' 1956 Memoir and these details will not be reproduced here.

At surface the Central mine merely amounted to a shaft, adit, Cornish beam pump and steam hoist, but at the South mine was a very considerable array of mining features of every description, as can be seen from the accompanying plan and photograph.

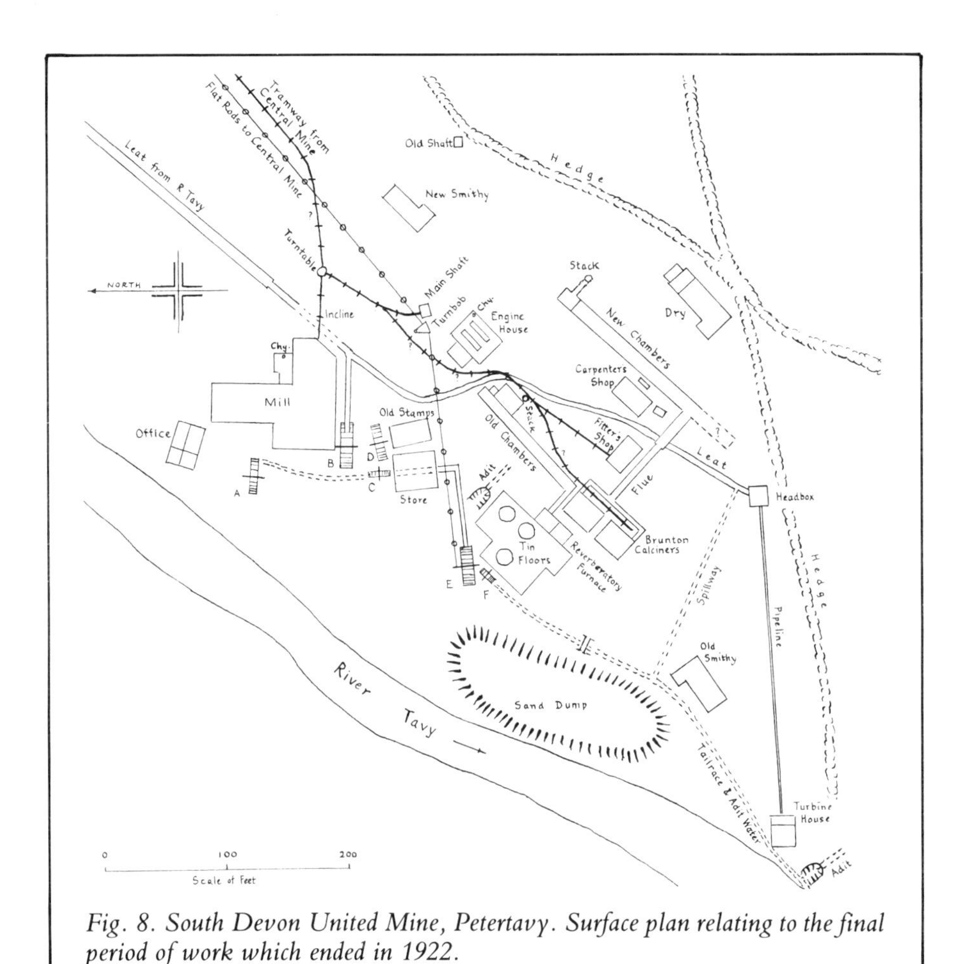

Fig. 8. South Devon United Mine, Petertavy. Surface plan relating to the final period of work which ended in 1922.

Plate XXIII. South Devon United Mine, possibly in 1905. The picture may be studied in conjunction with the accompanying plan, but it is impossible to photograph the site today as it is now completely screened by mature trees. (Photographer not known).

Plate XXIV. Main Shaft at South Devon United Mine in 1938 showing turnbob and pump rod (centre), fallen headgear, with inevitable notice "Trespassers will ... etc.," (right) and steam air compressor (far left). The chain below and to right of the notice was connected to the flat rod to the Central Mine.

In the final working it appears that ore from the shafts at both mines was brought to the turntable (see plan) in tramwagons which were then lowered down an incline to the mill where their contents were tipped onto a 2" grizzley, the "overs" being put through a Blake-Marsden jaw crusher. The resulting material went to a 10-head battery of Californian stamps thence to four Wilfley tables, six Frue vanners, two round frames and to rack frames.

Mill concentrates were then hauled back up the incline by a small "friction hoist" and trammed to the two Brunton calciners. I have no details of the friction hoist but it may have been akin to the warping drum on a ship's winch and was possibly steam-driven - a contemporary photograph (not reproduced here) shows a plume of smoke or steam coming from a chimney in its presumed vicinity.

Arsenical fumes from the Bruntons were condensed in a set of stone-built chambers in the normal way, while the burnt leavings or rinkle from the calciners went down to the adjoining tin floors where they are thought to have been ground in a Huntingdon mill - somewhat like a ball mill. Having been ground, the material was passed to a Wilfley table, three convex buddles, two slime tables, kieves and a magnetic separator - not necessarily in that order. Electricity is known to have

Plate XXV. The main shaft, South Devon United Mine, in 1938 showing the steam air compressor and turnbob. Though the view is the same as in the 1938 photograph, Roger Balkwill's sketch shows the roller support for the turnbob more clearly, also the chain which was connected to the flat rod to the Central Mine. (R.L. Balkwill).

***Plate XXVI. Same view of main shaft,** South Devon United Mine, but taken in 1983. Note that the iron ladder is still there, though it has since disappeared.*

been used on the mine and while it would obviously have been needed for the magnetic separator the tables and presumed Huntingdon mill may also have been electrically driven. The buddles, however, would almost certainly have been worked by the small waterwheel on the N.W. side of the building housing the tin floors and lettered "F" on the plan.

Electric power was provided by a dynamo driven by a large 6-foot diameter water turbine at the South mine which also operated an air-compressor supplying compressed air to both mines, while for periods of drought there was a steam-driven compressor sited immediately S.W. of the main shaft at the South mine.

A number of possible reasons for the closure of the mines have been put forward: shortage of water in a mine heavily dependent on water power and in this connection one wonders if the Great Drought of 1921 could have had something to do with it; the trade slump of the same

Plate XXVIII. Reverberatory furnace, South Devon United Mine, in 1990. There would originally have been an upper floor with an aperture (this is still open) down which ore would have been shovelled to the hearth below (this is inside and on the right). The firedoor is on the left, the cooling chamber bottom right, above which is the small working door through which the rabbling tool would have been inserted.

Plate XXVII. Shaft at Central Devon United Mine in 1989 showing knuckle joint between end of rocker bob and top of 6" square pump rod.

year; impoverishment of the mineral lodes; the fact that incoming water in the underground workings of the South mine was sometimes too heavy for the existing pump to hold unaided; difficulty in disposing of tailings, which could not be allowed to get into the Tavy; or a combination of some or all of these factors.

I first visited the mines in 1934 but did not make any detailed notes, nor take any photographs, until 1938. In the latter year I observed that at the Central mine there was a modern shaft fitted with cage-road, footway, headgear and beam pump and I noted that the last named was "worked by a waterwheel some way off" but did not record exactly where the wheel was sited. A leat from the Tavy en route for the South mine went under the dumps of the Central mine in a tunnel the north portal of which was inscribed "C.S. Ltd. 1918" for Contin Syndicate.

At the South mine there were a great many more items of interest. A shaft with fallen headgear but with turnbob and remains of pumping equipment in place was open and near the shaft head was a single-cylinder steam engine with twin flywheels direct coupled to a single-cylinder air compressor. On the site of the mill was a very large waterwheel, also (according to my notes) "several" smaller ones and the remains of sundry machinery including the two round frames, while nearby were two Brunton calciners with their attendant flues and arsenic condensing chambers. Finally at the southern end of the site was a shed containing the large water turbine and air compressor together with a concrete base for some other item, assumed to have been the dynamo.

At the Central Mine, in 1989, the shaft, complete with rocker-bob and 6" square wooden pump rod, still had timbering in place although filled in almost to surface. Until very recently the north portal of the leat tunnel under the dump, with inscription still discernible, was open but is now hidden under a pile of rocks (possibly put there because it was thought to be an entrance into the mine and therefore a potential hazard) so that this small piece of history has been lost.

The South mine is still rich in remains. Crossing the Tavy by the footbridge at the bottom of the lane from Marytavy Church and turning up the east bank the first feature to be noticed is the mouth of the adit on the South Lode and a few yards on is the turbine mentioned above, which was fed from the leat and headbox further up the hillside.

A little distance upriver and rather above the level of the bank are the ruins of the two Bruntons. Although most ironwork has been removed sufficient masonry is left to give some idea of how they worked but caution should be exercised when in their vicinity as the walls and flues are in a dangerously shaky state. Above the Bruntons are the vestiges of the set of stone-built arsenic condensing chambers; these are now so overgrown as to be hardly recognisable though a mere fifteen or so years ago it was possible to ascertain that each chamber measured about ten feet by six feet.

An interesting feature can be seen amid undergrowth near the N.W. corner of the northernmost Brunton. Although extremely ruinous it seems to have been a fairly conventional reverberatory furnace possibly pertaining to arsenic production in an earlier working, before the Bruntons were built. Its flue leads into what is assumed to have been an older set of chambers of which almost nothing now remains.

The Engine Shaft and concrete base for the steam-driven air compressor can be located, as can the cement floor of the mill building, but the pumping gear, steam engine itself and all mill machinery have now gone.

Plate XXIX. Site of mill, South Devon United Mine, in 1938 with waterwheel which powered it and in the foreground the remains of the two round frames.

All waterwheels have of course by now disappeared but most of their wheelpits can still be located and the following details may be read in conjunction with the accompanying plan:-

Reference Letters	Internal size of wheelpits in feet	Items driven by former wheels
A	28 x 4	Possibly mill machinery in earlier working
B	34 x 9	Mill machinery in final working
C	20 x 7 (?)	Not known
D	34 x 7	Cornish stamps in earlier working
E	28 x 7	Beam pumps at Central and South mines
F	10 x 3	Buddles on tin floors

The turbine, though rusted up and now lacking its rotor, has rather surprisingly survived. It is understood to be of the Thompson "inward flow" variety, the amount and direction of the water impinging on the central rotor or "runner" having been controlled by four moveable vanes.

Plate XXX. Large water turbine at South Devon United Mine in 1989 with Philip Densham, author's son-in-law, standing beside it.

When I first saw it, these were connected by gearing to a single control handwheel, but now only the keyed shafts carrying the individual vanes are left. It originally drove an air compressor (part of which was still lying in the mud of the tailrace in 1990) and a dynamo (long since removed). It is possible that such a turbine, given an adequate head of water and driving a dynamo, could have produced an output of about 200 Kw.

In conclusion it must be stressed that while everything looks very neat and tidy on the plan the state of affairs today is very different. The majority of the buildings, having been of timber or corrugated iron, were probably removed soon after the abandonment and evidence of their existence now has to be sought among nearly seventy years' growth of trees and other vegetation, while even stonebuilt structures are exceedingly incomplete and decrepit.

The Reverend Hugh Breton, writing in 1912 of the attractiveness of the valley, added somewhat sourly "Of late years a wretched mine has spoiled this spot of some of its charm. As I saw it fourteen years ago, before the hand of man had marred the scene, it was undoubtedly one of the most beautiful nooks on the moor". If the Rev. Breton were able to revisit the valley today I think that he would find that it has regained much of the former charm that he remembered, such mining features as are not now hidden by vegetation having been transformed into picturesque ivy-clad ruins.

CHAPTER 6

SOME MINES NEAR ILSINGTON
(Grid Refs. as given in text)

A SMALL AND OBSCURE BUT NEVERTHELESS interesting corner of the local mining scene is to be found in the vicinity of Lewthorne Cross, half a mile west of Ilsington Church. Here were situated the three mines of Albion, Atlas and Smallacombe which worked sometimes jointly and sometimes independently for iron, tin, ochre and umber between the 1830s and the 1920s. Apart from a short period of idleness in the mid-1880s one or other of the mines was in being, if not actually producing, from 1858 to 1908, while as recently as 1920 a few tons of black tin were mined under the name of Albion.

Three geographical locations are involved, one immediately N.W. of the cross with two moderately deep shafts named White's and Sarl's and marked "Atlas Mine" on the 1906 six-inch Ordnance map (778762), the second a large open work half a mile N.N.W. of the cross and on the west side of the road to Haytor marked "Smallacombe Cutting" (777766) and the third a quarter of a mile east of the centre of Smallacombe Cutting and on the east of the road to Middlecott where a number of mining features including an adit and tramway are marked "Tin Mine - disused" (781765).

Written details and statistical data about the mines exist in plenty but when examined closely one may be left in doubt, even when names are given, as to which of the geographical locations they refer. Matters are further complicated by the fact that both near-vertical tin lodes and gently sloping beds of iron ore occurred in the same area, the two minerals having been worked at different times (or on occasion at the same time) by different companies.

Regarding underground workings at and near Smallacombe, H.G. Dines' 1956 memoir states that "deep adit commences 200 yards east of the open work" but as the latter measures about 250 yards from east to west and 130 yards from north to south the location he gave is not a very precise one. The likeliest location for the deep adit mouth (there was also a shallow adit higher up and further to the west) seems to be the one referred to under "Tin Mine - disused" above, which is some 250 yards E.S.E. of the centre of the cutting.

It may be surmised that while the name "Smallacombe" implies the definite location of the cutting, "Atlas" may have implied either the workings just N.W. of Lewthorne Cross, or at Smallacombe, or both.

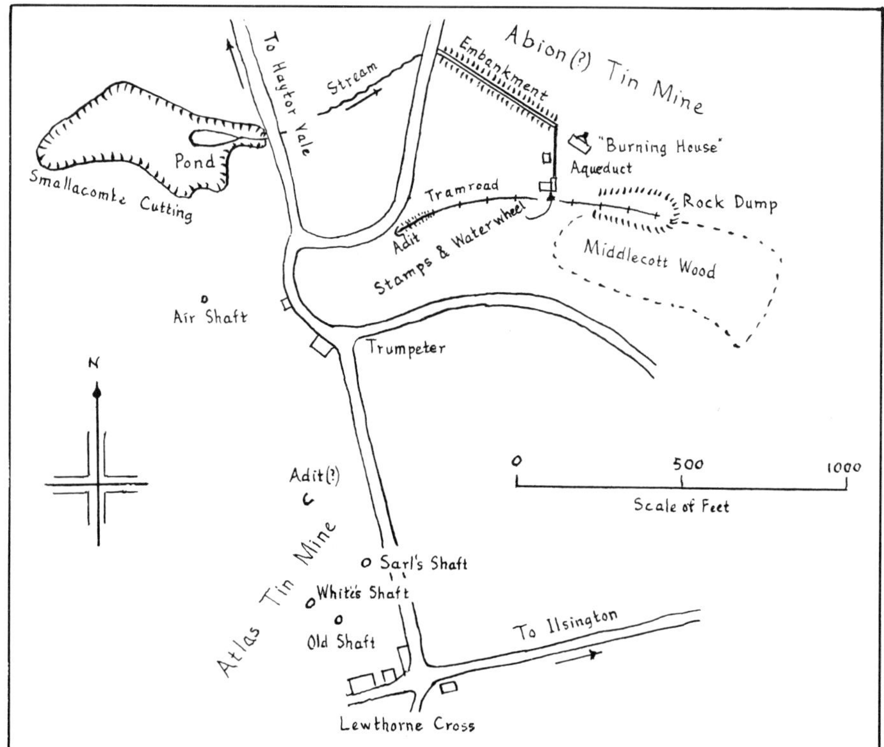

Fig. 9. Mining features in the vicinity of Lewthorne Cross, Smallacombe Cutting and Middlecott Wood, Ilsington.

The name "Albion" was in use in the 1830s though at that time lacking a location and the name was revived in the early 20th century when it embraced all three locations, although the deep adit referred to above was probably the main centre of activity.

Going on to firmer ground (though not literally, as will be seen presently) the area of greater interest today is in the vicinity of the deep adit mouth as shown on the accompanying sketch plan, but is on private land belonging to Mr. A.S. Courtier of Haytor, from whom permission to enter must first be obtained. A.K. Hamilton Jenkin, in his *Mines of Devon* (1981) quoting from the *Mining Journals* of 1859 and 1860 and referring to White's and Sarl's shafts, said that from 1860 "ore from (these) shafts and adit was conveyed by tramway to Middlecott Wood, a short distance to the east where a 60-foot stamps wheel together with two calciners and an accompanying stack were erected by the side of a small stream." I am inclined to doubt whether there was ever a tramway from Lewthorne Cross to Middlecott Wood (the latter is in any case

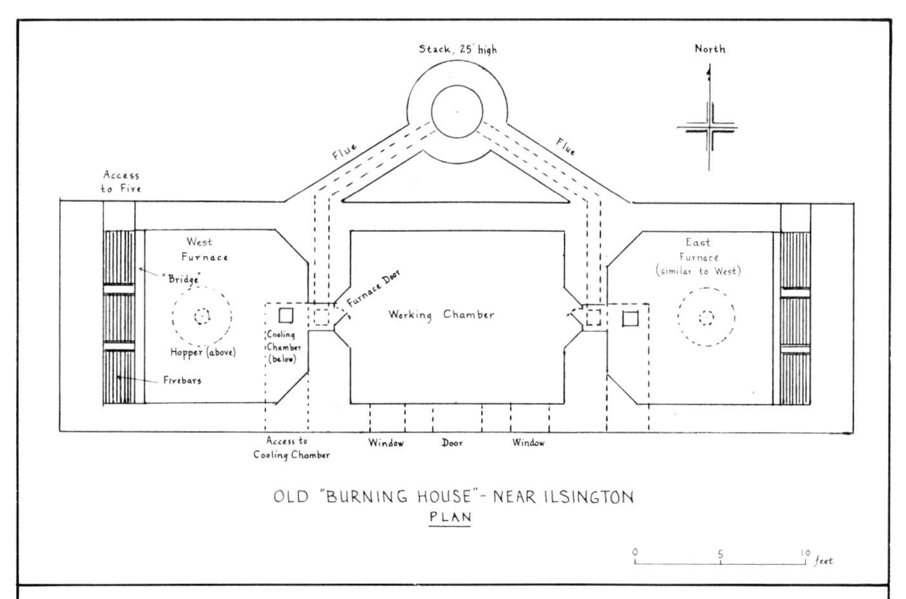

Fig. 10. Plan and elevations of the old "Burning House" at Albion Mine, Ilsington.

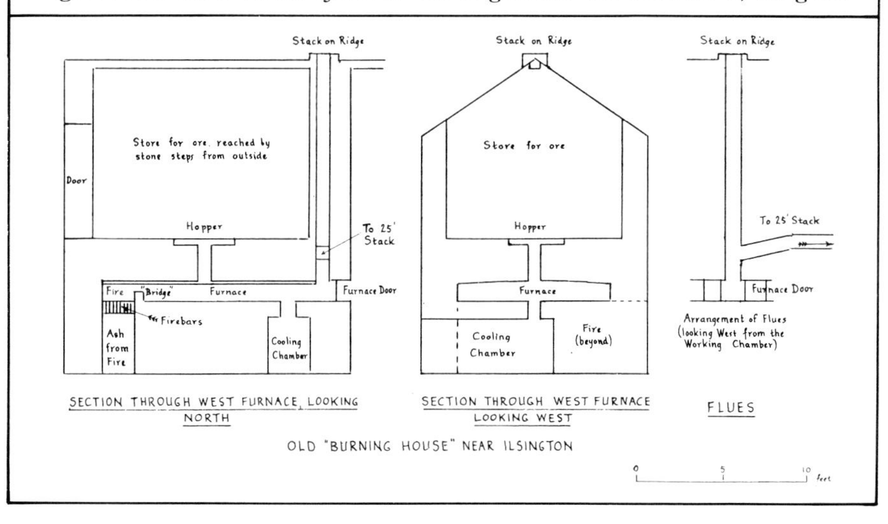

north of the cross not east of it) but feel that the tramway referred to is more likely to have been the one leading east from the deep adit to the stamps and dump. Further, mention of a 60-foot wheel seems suspect, 20-feet being more probable, but the reference to calciners and stack is entirely correct as these items are still there today, though surrounded by thick undergrowth and swampy ground which even at the height of the 1989 drought was a veritable morass.

Plate XXXI. Door of one of the two reverberatory furnaces in the old "Burning House" at Albion Mine in 1990.

Plate XXXII. Door and windows of the working chamber of the old "Burning House" at Albion Mine in 1990. On either side of these are accesses to the cooling chambers while the stack, now completely covered in ivy, and the two fire doors are on the other side of the building.

Within this piece of ground a number of other features can still be seen, including the approximate site of the adit mouth, now collapsed and heavily overgrown but with a stream flowing along the tramway cutting leading from it. The track of the tramway is traceable eastward as far as a quite substantial tree-covered dump, passing on its way immediately behind a stone-built wheelpit which would have accommodated a wheel about 20 feet in diameter. It is known that the stamps were situated directly beside this wheel on its west side and that the noise from them could be heard as far away as Haytor Vale.

Water for the wheel was obtained from a small stream flowing down from Smallacombe Cutting, this being conveyed along an earth embankment to the vicinity of the calciner building or "Burning House," from which it was carried to the wheel by an overhead launder. Unusual features of the embankment are firstly its size — its flat top being upwards of 20 feet wide and the base considerably wider — and secondly the fact that it does not lead directly towards the stamps wheel. Its size seems over-generous if it was only required to carry a mere thread of water and one would have thought that a raised launder would have been an easier and cheaper solution, but it is known that immense amounts of over-burden would have had to be dug out when working the Smallacombe Cutting and the embankment may have been a convenient way of disposing of some of it. As to direction, this may have been chosen in order to keep to fairly level ground, perhaps following the line of a former field hedge, and avoiding the swampy area near the stamps wheel. Theorising further, ore from other sections of the mine could have been conveyed along the top of the embankment to the calciners, but this is conjecture.

By far the most interesting feature is the Burning House, which due to its subsequent use as a hay barn has survived almost intact, as shown in the drawings. The building, flues and adjoining stack, all dating from the 1860s (though possibly slightly modified at a later date) are built of local stone, the building and stack being in a good state of preservation (the latter largely held together by the ivy which completely envelopes it) but the flues from the furnaces have crumbled.

The twin furnaces are of the reverberatory type, where the charge does not come into direct contact with the fuel used for firing (the firebars, shown in the drawings for the sake of clarity, have in fact been removed), ore from the floor above being shovelled into the shallow hoppers and so down to the furnace hearths below. The roasting ore would have been rabbled with long-handled implements inserted through the furnace doors from the working chamber and when sufficiently calcined would have been raked into the holes leading to the cooling chambers below. This roasting of ore was carried out partly to drive off unwanted constituents and partly to render the ore more amenable to subsequent processes. Looking at the drawings, a puzzling question is the relationship between the horizontal flues leading to the detached 25-foot stack and those leading vertically to the two ridge stacks on the roof of the building and the apparent absence of any dampers to control the flow of furnace gases between the two sets of flues. But in general the surviving features present a textbook picture, rendering the functioning of this type of furnace very easy to understand.

CHAPTER 7

THE SHINING ORE MINES OF THE BOVEY TRACEY DISTRICT
(Grid. Refs. as given in text.)

THE AREA OF GRANITE IMMEDIATELY NORTH AND north west of Bovey Tracey is traversed by numerous east-west veins of "specular iron," an oxide of iron occurring in minute blackish mica-like flakes, sometimes known as micaceous iron, whose splendent lustre also earned it the name "looking-glass ore" or "shining ore".

This shining ore was mined from the beginning of the 19th century or possibly earlier by over a dozen small concerns in the area, often working somewhat intermittently, and mostly employing up to half a dozen, or at most a dozen men each. In former days considerable quantities of the ore were sold as "Devonshire Sand" or "Pounce," a powder which before the introduction of blotting paper was sprinkled on wet ink in order to dry it. Latterly it was sold as a base for anti-corrosion paints, including the well known "battleship grey" of the Royal Navy. It proved unusually suitable for making this type of paint as the crystalline flakes in their natural state were of a most favourable shape and size, overlapping each other to form an impervious layer which resisted corrosion. I have been told that the only other location producing similar ore is in Austria but that the flakes found there are larger and therefore less suitable for this purpose.

The method of mining was simple: trial pits were sunk in a likely spot on a hillside until a workable vein or lode was located, on which horizontal tunnels or adits were then driven and the ore excavated. The latter was often so soft that it could be removed with picks and shovels though harder portions might have to be taken out by means of rock drills and blasting.

In earlier days the harder ore removed from a lode was trammed to a stamping mill after which the fine material from the stamps was subjected to the action of a stream of water flowing along a "sluice box" in which the waste material accompanying it fell to the bottom while the thin mica-like flakes were carried on in suspension to settling pits. As the ore in the pits settled the water was gradually drained off until only the ore was left which was then dug out, dried and sold. Softer material did not have to be stamped but went direct to the sluice boxes. These sluice boxes were not a particularly efficient means of treating the ore and in later years more sophisticated methods were employed, as will be described later on in this chapter.

Plate XXXIII. Old circular buddles at Wray Mine in 1990.

With the exception of Great Rock and Kelly the mines were very small and not all were particularly successful even though some of them were sometimes worked jointly with neighbouring mines. These smaller mines will first be described briefly; notwithstanding the fact that some of them were abandoned before 1914, so are strictly speaking outside the time-scale of this book, these will be included for the sake of completeness.

Wray 771848

Worked for micaceous iron ore in the 1920s as "Wray Barton" then from 1929 until 1938 for red ochre (another iron ore) as "Wray", the implication being that there were two separate sites. Walking south west towards Wray Barton Farm in the Summer of 1938 I noted that on Pepperdown, overlooking the Barton, was a site comprising the concrete bases of three circular buddles and the remains of a drying furnace and its chimney, with much micaceous iron ore lying around in the vicinity. The general state of the site did not suggest that there had been any very recent activity, so it is assumed that it related to the 1920s Wray Barton working, though at the time I knew nothing of the past history of the area and had come upon the site by chance.

Revisiting the place in the Spring of 1990 I was surprised to find that the interval of over 50 years seemed to have had little effect on it and it was exactly as I remembered it from 1938. I did, however, note the possible site of a collapsed adit just above it, and I also wondered how sufficient water could have been obtained for ore-dressing. It could possibly have been piped from the Wray Brook, 200 yards to the east, but the amount available would have been very minimal. It is understood that there were a couple more adits somewhere in the vicinity of the brook but a search for these, hampered by bramble thickets and fallen trees, was unsuccessful.

Pepperdown — Vicinity of 778850?

Opened up for micaceous iron in the early 1940s but ceased operations in 1944. Its exact location is not known to me, but is assumed to be near the Wray mines mentioned above and may have been little more than a prospect.

Laployd Down — 805852

An old mine, probably no more than a trial, in what is now Laployd Plantation, where the 1906 6" Ordnance Map marks three old shafts.

Moorwood — 777837

This was a much more recent mine, the reason for its existence being that the ore produced from Wray proved unsatisfactory for paint manufacture so that in 1931 their management carried out further prospecting in the area to find more suitable lodes, which were duly located in Moor Wood, about 500 yards S.W. of Lewdons Farm, and some way to the south of Wray. Records about Moorwood appear scanty but when travelling down the A.382 in 1951 I noted modern buildings also a chimney which may have been smoking though I could not be too sure of this, producing an appearance of possible activity, but I was not able to stop and investigate. Round about the same time I was told by a Mr Parsons of Christow that the mine had recently been opened up, however.

A visit in 1966 showed the site to be abandoned, with a mill building on two levels containing only concrete bases for former machinery items though some electrical switchgear was still in place while nearby were the customary settling pits. In early 1974 the building was being dismantled and by the middle of that year it was evident that a dwelling house was being built on the site.

Shuttamoor — 825827

Situated about 1/4 mile E.S.E. of the farm of that name and worked from 1897 or earlier until 1911, for the most part in conjunction with other small mines in the vicinity. A contemporary photograph shows the Shuttamoor mill to have been a timber and corrugated iron building containing a small battery of Californian stamps driven by a water wheel, the latter presumably being fed from the nearby stream flowing east to the Canonteign Waterfall.

Sycamore — Vicinity of 825828?

A small mine of which nothing appears to be known beyond the fact that it was somewhere near Shuttamoor.

Hawkmoor — 799818

Another small mine, operated variously with other neighbouring concerns from 1892 to 1902, though it may have been previously worked as far back as the 1860s. It was acquired by the Ferrubron Company in 1902 in which year that company also acquired Great Rock but elected to close Hawkmoor immediately.

Visiting the site in 1973 I noted some overgrown settling pits some 580 yards north of Slade Cross and on the south side of a stream flowing W.S.W., while nearby were several old adits and other remains.

Shaptor — 806809

Employed a dozen or so men in the 1890s and was acquired by the Ferrubron Co. in 1902, after which it was worked with Shuttamoor until closing in about 1911 or possibly a year or so later. In 1972 several old shafts were to be seen on the S.W. side of Shaptor Rock, the Rock itself being 700 yards W.S.W. of Beadon Cross. The 1906 6" Ordnance Map marks "Windpump" 100 yards south of the Rock; as this was very close to the marked position of an air shaft I felt that the windpump could have been something to do with the mine but a search failed to reveal any trace of the former existence of such an item. There are some concrete settling tanks by the stream flowing down past the S.E. side of the former Hawkmoor Sanatorium, and about 20 yards upstream from the tanks is a concreted recess measuring 4 feet by 9 inches and 14 inches deep with a substantial holding down bolt on each side of it evidently for some small machinery item; an opinion has been expressed that the latter might have been a pelton wheel.

Bowden Hill, or Bowden Down — 819809

An old mine, said to have been active in 1877, and represented today by an open work 600 yards long running approximately W.S.W./E.N.E. with its centre 1,100 yards west of Hennock Church.

When visiting the Geological Survey Library in London in 1958 and writing my name in the Visitors' Book I noticed a nearby entry suggesting that someone was currently taking an interest in "Bowden mine, Bovey Tracey" and in 1972 I was told that an adit could still be seen there - presumably the one described by H.G. Dines (1956) as being 300 yards N.W. of Chericombe Head, though looking at the 6" map 220 yards seems likelier.

Plumley 804807

Situated 650 yards W.S.W. of Shaptor Rock and immediately S.E. of the former Hawkmoor Sanatorium. Active from 1896 to 1911 having been operated latterly by the Ferrubron Co. On the S.E. side of the stream flowing past the S.E. side the former Sanatorium and about 200 yards from the road from Bovey Tracey to Moretonhampstead are possible vestiges of dressing floors and settling pits, and further up the hillside to the S.E. are collapsed adits and quite substantial dumps, but in 1990 the area was very overgrown.

North Combe Shining Ore 804807?

The only evidence of the existence of this mine appears to be in the Official Mines List for 1895. No detailed return was given for that year but the ownership and name of Chief Agent were the same as shown for Plumley, the latter being situated in North Combe Copse, with its recorded statistics commencing in 1896 so it seems to be more than a possibility that North Combe and Plumley were alternative names for the same mine.

Going on to the last two mines in the area, namely Great Rock and Kelly, not only were they the most important of the shining ore producers but they were each noteworthy for other reasons which will be disclosed presently.

Great Rock 818816

Began work in the mid-19th century or perhaps even earlier under the name "Hennock Iron and Tin Mine", which apparently occupied two separate sites, the "Tin Mine" (if it existed at all) being elsewhere. In 1902 the "Iron Mine" was taken over by the Ferrubron Co. which re-named it Great Rock after the nearby granite outcrop of that name, and it enjoyed the distinction of not only working continuously for the 67 years from 1902 to 1969 but also of being the last metal mine in Devon to close down.

The underground workings are situated under the high ground immediately east of Beadon Lane, on five parallel lodes running approximately east-west and named North Beadon, Main Beadon, North, Middle and Main South. The Beadon lodes and the western end of Main South lode were worked by adits driven east from beside Beadon Lane while North, Middle and the eastern end of Main South were worked by adits driven west from Lake's Copse in the deep valley on the east side of the high ground. The mill buildings, workshops, office, etc., were also sited in this valley, near a small stream flowing north to join the Beadon Brook, while the drying shed, where the processed ore

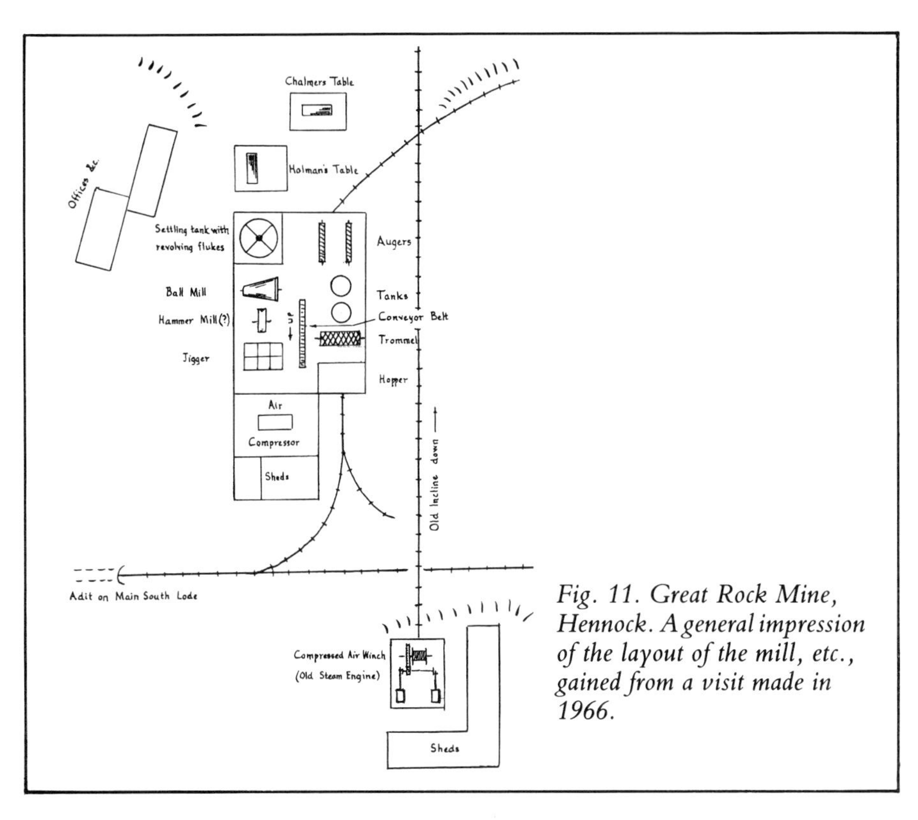

Fig. 11. Great Rock Mine, Hennock. A general impression of the layout of the mill, etc., gained from a visit made in 1966.

Plate XXXIV. Mill at Great Rock Mine in course of being dismantled in 1970. In foreground is the ball mill.

was dried and packed, was a little way down the Beadon Brook itself.

I was taken round the mine, both above and below ground, in the summer of 1966 by Mr Wills, the manager, who kindly gave me several hours of his time. We entered the underground workings by an adit driven on Main South lode from near the mill buildings, and I noted that working platforms or stagings were built across the line of the lode some 15 feet above each other with vertical gaps every few yards to leave space alternatively for ladderways and ore chutes. Having gained access to a working face via a ladderway (these disappeared up into the gloom to an alarming height) the miners threw the good ore down the nearest chute and piled waste onto the staging. Though the lodes were only a foot or so wide a working width of at least four feet was necessary to get at the ore, so a good deal of waste rock had to be taken out and disposed of in that way. Ore was trammed to the mill in wagons drawn by an 18" gauge battery-driven electric locomotive capable of drawing a train of up to eight wagons. Two such locomotives had been improvised on the mine.

Originally the mill had consisted of a small battery of Californian stamps together with the customary sluice boxes, but it was subsequently modernised, the stamps being replaced by a ball mill and other items such as jiggers, concentrating tables, etc., added. Until the 1920s power was provided by waterwheels but these were replaced successively by a water turbine, a diesel engine (which also drove an air compressor) and finally, in about 1950, by electric power from the National Grid.

Processed ore was piped or laundered down to the drying shed as slurry where it was passed to a succession of concrete tanks in the first of which the coarser ore settled then in succeeding tanks medium ore, fine ore and slimes. After settling, the material was dug out, dried in oil-fired furnaces, packed and despatched, while surplus water was pumped back to the mill for re-use. Half a dozen men were employed - two miners, an ore-dresser who also worked underground on occasion, a driver and loader, a fitter, together with Mr Wills who concerned himself with safety and gave general assistance as necessary. The output was said to have been about 600 tons a year.

To reproduce all the information gained on my visit would make this chapter over long, but one further detail must be added. As I was about to take my leave, having looked at the mine plans kept in the office, Mr Wills said he had one more thing to show me, and produced a wooden box such as scientific instruments are kept in, with an ivorine tally plate on its lid bearing the words "The Revealer", with the name of an instrument maker added in smaller letters. Taken out of the box it proved to be the modern equivalent of a traditional divining rod, consisting of two handgrips, in each of which could be fitted a slender metal rod, graduated along its length, and capable of swivelling horizontally. The two handgrips were joined by a bridge so that they were held a foot or so apart with the rods inclined slightly downwards and (when at rest) parallel to each other, while in the centre of the bridge was a recess in which one of a selection of small glass phials could be inserted. There was a rack of about ten of these phials in the box, each marked as containing a different substance which, Mr Wills explained, would if placed in the recess cause the rods to respond to that same substance if present in the ground over which the Revealer passed. Response was indicated by the rods crossing each other, the place at which they crossed being a measure of the depth at which the substance might be expected, hence the graduations. At this point I was considering pinching myself to make sure that I was really awake and hearing all this, but noticing one apparently empty phial marked "void" I asked what this meant. Mr Wills said that if used this phial would cause the Revealer to respond to empty cavities underground, and proceeded to relate a curious story:— When the management was considering investing in a Revealer the maker's representative undertook to demonstrate it, so was taken up onto the hill above the underground workings (whereabouts of which were known to Mr Wills but not, it was thought, to the representative) and asked to describe what he detected. The latter successfully followed the course of an adit beneath with the aid of the phial marked "void" but after some distance stopped and remarked "there is something odd here as at this point the adit seems to be twice its normal width". This was apparently quite correct as they were over a place where a lode had divided and initially the miners had followed what they thought was the more promising branch, but this had proved incorrect so they had had to return and pursue the other one, resulting in the unusual width of the drive at that spot.*

Sadly the payable ore became exhausted (even the Revealer could not locate ore where none existed) and the mine closed down some three years later, in 1969.

Not knowing of the closure I had, however, some reason to suspect in 1970 that something might have happened (among other things the mine had gone off the telephone) so decided to make a further visit. This I did in August of that year and found the place deserted and everything in disarray, giving the appearance of having been abandoned for a year or more. Doors were open and windows broken but though some mill machinery had been removed most of it was still there. A

* Divining or dowsing can be achieved in a similar manner using two wire coathangers, suitably cut into ┌ shapes. Dowsing is looked upon with sceptisism by many but appears to work for some individuals (Ed.).

union card for "S. Tremain" lying on the floor of the blacksmith's shop showed his last deduction to have been made in February 1969.

Two months later the remaining plant, etc., was being dismantled and taken away, though I was able to take some photographs and make a sketch plan. But by then the jiggers, which I had particularly wished to examine closely, had unfortunately been reduced to a heap of twisted scrap metal, though the tables and ball mill had still survived intact.

The drying shed had somehow escaped the attentions of the scrap dealers up to that time and I was able to investigate it fairly thoroughly the following month although not all the items in it could be identified, partly due to lack of light in its inner recesses. Everything has now gone though it is understood that the building itself was dismantled relatively recently.

In 1973, I had a conversation with an elderly man who had once been the blacksmith at Great Rock and who furnished some further information. He established his credibility by telling me that the mine was once run by two Germans, one named Gartzke and the other Hans - the official Mines List for 1901-1902 gives the ownership at that time as G. Gartzke & Co., so perhaps that company was connected with the Austrian specular iron location. He quoted the names of subsequent managers as Slatter and Tucker - again correct, the Mines Lists showing E.M. Slatter as manager in 1925 and E. Tucker in 1950. He said that Tucker was a very prudent manager who, as soon as a lode was located and proved, would move his development team on to find another, while according to my informant subsequent managers merely went round working out Tucker's reserves without trying to develop fresh ones. His opinion was that it had been a mistake to introduce electricity on the mine, which greatly added to the working costs when they already had adequate water power available costing little or nothing. He was also critical of certain aspects of the system under which the miners were paid which, he said, was some sort of piecework arrangement which on occasion resulted in an undue amount of good ore finding its way onto the dump.

Kelly 795818

Although not as important as Great Rock, Kelly had an almost equally long record of activity - 55 years between 1879 and 1944, with an eight-year break between 1892 and 1900. But what is equally noteworthy is that although abandoned over 45 years ago and situated within a few yards of a busy road, the buildings and machinery have survived almost intact to this day. It was the hope of the late Frank Booker (author of *The Industrial Archaeology of the Tamar Valley* etc.) that the interesting features at Kelly might somehow be preserved for posterity instead of

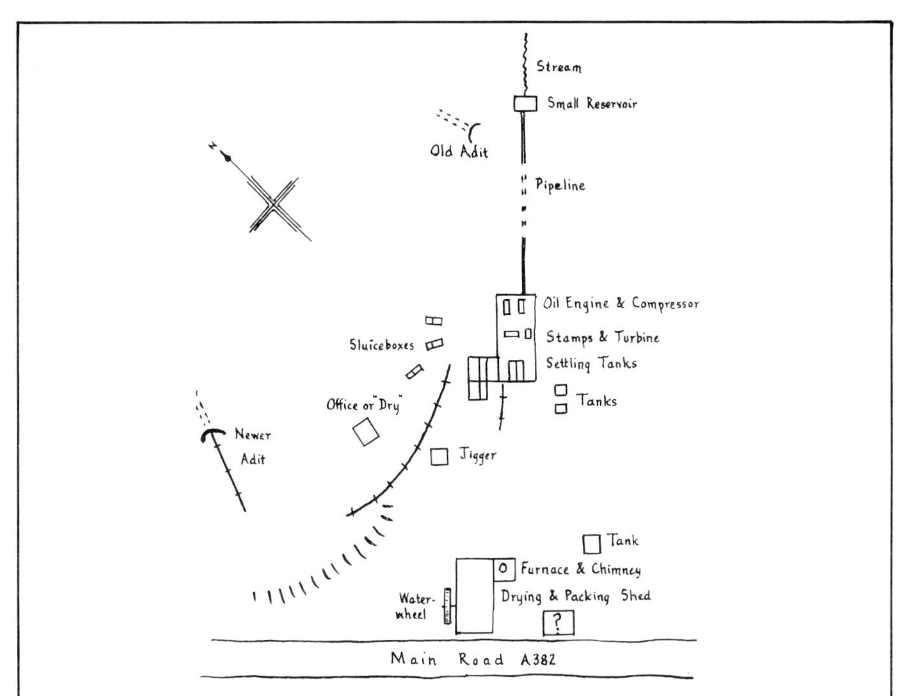

Fig. 12. Kelly Mine, Lustleigh. Sketch plan made in 1952 showing sundry surface features, most of which have survived to the present day.

Plate XXXV. Mill building, Kelly Mine, in 1952, with hand operated jigger in foreground.

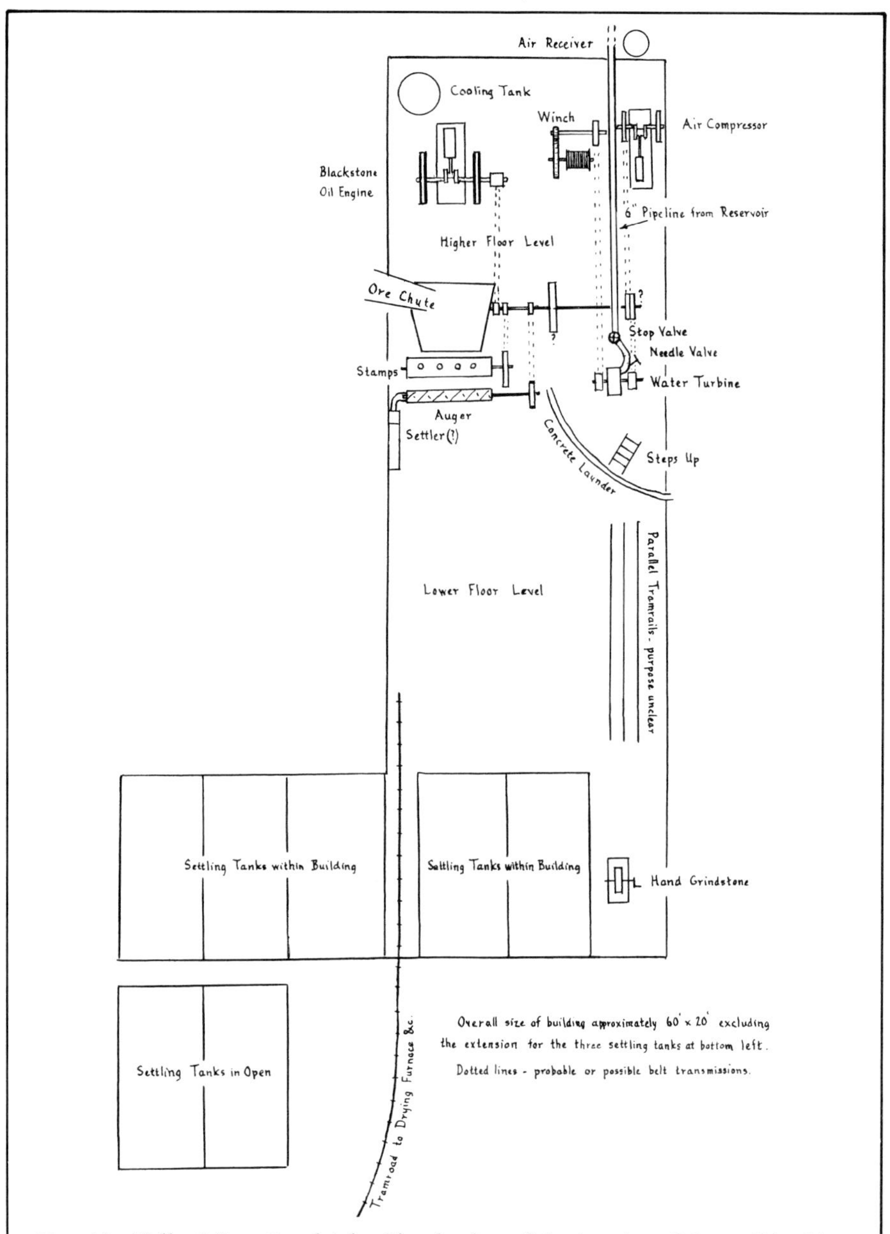

Fig. 13. Kelly Mine, Lustleigh. Sketch plan of the interior of the mill building made in 1966.

Mr Peter Roberts, of the Kelly Mine Preservation Society, has told me that very recent investigations indicated that the winch was used to haul wagons up an incline sited to the left of the building, by a cable led round pulleys to the top of the incline.

being left to decay and slowly fall into ruin. Although Frank did not live to see his wish fulfilled the mine site has now been leased by the Kelly Mine Preservation Society whose members are making strenuous efforts to put things to rights and to prevent further deterioration. Permission to visit must be obtained, either from the Society or from the nearby Kelly Farm.

In its earlier life Kelly had a succession of different owners, but from about 1920 onwards it was run by the same company which operated Great Rock - the Ferrubron Co. - and initially the same manager, E.M. Slatter, looked after both mines.

The main buildings are situated on the N.E. side of the Bovey Tracey to Moretonhampstead road some 800 yards N.W. of Slade Cross and consist of a timber-framed mill building some 30 yards in from the road and an older stone building at the very edge of the road, the latter having a waterwheel beside its N.W. wall and a drying furnace and chimney on its S.E. side. There are several adits in the vicinity, the principal one being about 30 yards N.W. of the buildings just mentioned. Although most of the other shining ore mines were worked by adit only, any shafts being merely air shafts, thus obviating pumping and hoisting costs, a working shaft was actually sunk at Kelly with a view to proving the ore at depth. It is said to have been "in front of the adit" (presumably the principal one referred to above) and when C.F. Barclay and R.W. Toll visited the mine in 1921, by which time the shaft had been abandoned and covered over, they noted the presence of the iron rocker bob of a small Cornish pump, also the remains of a winch, but they did not record what the motive power for these items had been.

The stone building directly beside the road is something of an enigma, as while the drying furnace is a straightforward item, varying views have been put forward regarding the purpose of the waterwheel. Some suggest that it might have powered a fan for drying ore but my informant, the ex-blacksmith from Great Rock, thought it had driven some sort of ore separating device embodying an archimedean screw or auger. I will hazard a guess and suggest that the building could have housed the original mill machinery, dating perhaps from 1879 and that it was later superseded by the more modern mill. The floor of the older building consists of three stepped levels (a normal feature of such mills) and a report dated about 1919 recorded that the ore was crushed by a battery of Cornish (sic) stamps worked by an overshot waterwheel. In the 1960s I noted that the wheel was connected to overhead shafting by gearing giving a fourfold increase in speed of revolution which would seem consistent with the operation of a small stamp battery while the archimedean screw (again a common feature in such mills) could have been worked from the same shafting.

Plate XXXVI. Californian stamps at Kelly Mine, 1966.

In contrast, Barclay and Toll's report of 1921 says that the ore was crushed by a battery of small *Californian* stamps worked by a water turbine - these presumably being the same items which are in the new mill today - and suggesting that the latter was built round about 1920, i.e. the date when the Ferrubron Co. took over; but contrary to this theory it has to be said that the 2nd Edition 6" Ordnance map shows that there was a building of sorts on the site of the new mill as far back as 1906. However, after the old roadside building ceased to fulfill its original function (whatever that was) there seems little doubt that it was used as a drying and packing shed; in fact on an early visit I noticed a large container containing a quantity of 2" wooden bungs for barrels standing in a corner.

My first visit to the mine was in 1952, only seven years after the abandonment, when everything was reaonably intact, but from then until the preservation society took over I noted a gradual deterioration.

As recently as 1966 the Californian stamps were in good order and it was still possible to start up the turbine by opening its inlet valve, but by 1970 the bearing brasses of the stamps axle had been taken, rendering the stamps inoperable and by 1983 the cover of the turbine rotor had been removed. In the early seventies there were at least two tipping wagons standing on the tramroad below the mill which now seem to have disappeared, while in February, 1978, a heavy fall of snow brought down part of the mill roof. It is understood that the members of the preservation society are gradually dealing with these and other matters.

One further point of interest which may be mentioned is that when visiting the site some 20 years ago I noticed for the first time an inconspicuous telegraph post among the trees above the mill. Investigating further I found that it was the first of a line of such posts which led me to the remains of a dwelling, almost totally concealed in foliage, and consisting of a small but substantial stonebuilt house to the front and to one end of which had been added a timber and glass conservatory. This I assumed to have been the manager's house, and on looking round for possible clues as to the date of its last occupancy I came upon a pile of partly pulped magazines, dated around about 1944 and apparently dealing with mystical or astrological matters. Having been told that at Great Rock there was faith in divining I felt almost inclined to wonder whether at Kelly they worked the mine according to signs in the stars. This house is some 200 yards N.E. of the mill building and though now in an advanced state of decay, with roof fallen in and most of the conservatory gone, the ground round it is more open than formerly, making it quite easy to locate.

CHAPTER 8

BRIDFORD BARYTES MINE
829864

BRIDFORD MINE, JUST EAST OF BRIDFORD VILLAGE and in a small lateral valley leading down to the River Teign, is noteworthy as the only mine in S.W. England to have produced the mineral barytes (sulphate of barium) commercially on a large scale, also because it was a big mine employing 100 or more men and further was almost the last mine in Devon to close down.

Barytes is used in paint manufacture, in the production of hydrogen peroxide and in connection with the drilling of oil wells and has many other commercial applications. In the Teign Valley it occurred most plentifully at the northern end of a north-south barytic-lead lode which runs northward from a point about ½ mile east of Hennock Village up to the vicinity of Bridford, and a number of lead mines were situated along its length. Pieces of barytes can be found today on many of the old dumps of waste rock bordering the road up the valley and are easily recognisable by their white colour and the fact that they are half as heavy again as pieces of ordinary rock.

Work began in a small way in the 1850s when a few tons of barytes were produced from an open work, almost certainly sited at 829866, after which matters lapsed until 1876 when limited underground work began under the name of Teign Valley Mine, a dozen or so men being employed and the ore being sent to Exeter for processing.

According to a newspaper article written in 1949 the mine was acquired in 1926 by Lt. Col. J.V. Ramsden and his cousin Sir John Ramsden whose company began to develop it vigorously under the name of Bridford. The main shaft was deepened, soon reaching 380 feet, a new mill using modern methods was built on the spot and the workforce was increased to about 100. Activity built up in the 1940s under the managership of Mr P.J. Tonkin, and the workings reached a depth of 500 feet while production increased to a peak of 24,000 tons a year.

In 1950, however, the mine was taken over by another company and my impression was that the Ramsdens had been manoeuvred into a position where loss of their control of it had become inevitable.

Activity appears to have dwindled after that and, although some development at depth is said to have been carried out, the mine finally closed in the late summer of 1958, probably on 31st July.

Concerning the reasons for the closure, several versions have been put forward. One report said that the ore bodies had shown not only signs of exhaustion at depth but also increasing contamination by

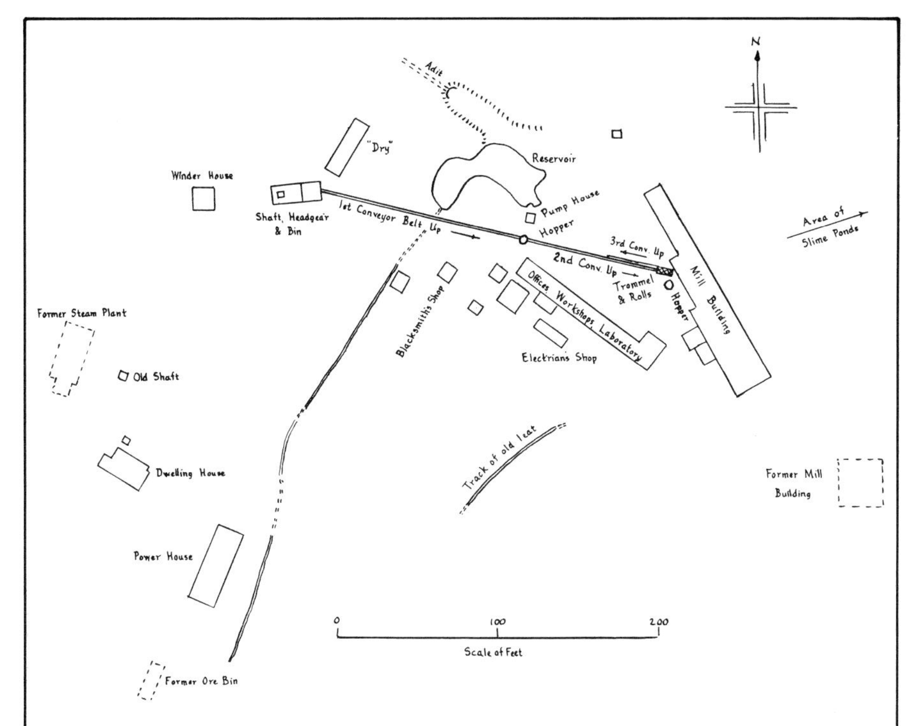

Fig. 14. Bridford Mine. Sketch plan of the surface workings made in 1962, four years after the closure, based on a plan of the mine.

sulphides of iron, lead and zinc. Another said that the reason was reduced demand for barytes and the fact that the mine was virtually worked out. A third said that ore was thought to exist in payable quantities at greater depth but to prove it would have required either a new shaft or costly repairs to the existing one and that the company concerned was not prepared to put up the extra money.

I was aware of the mine's existence as far back as 1938 and finding myself unexpectedly in the area on 12th June of that year decided to take advantage of the opportunity to pay a visit there. Calling at a nearby dwelling to make some general enquiries, fortune favoured me as it proved to be the house of the manager, Mr. Tonkin, although I did not know this at the time. I think he must have realised that I was a genuine seeker after knowledge (and had perhaps even acquired a little already) for he went to great trouble to show me round, even taking me underground so that I could see the lode — to get there we had to climb down the ladders because being a Sunday the winding machinery was not in use. And on my taking my leave he presented me with a small cluster of perfectly formed barytes crystals.

Plate XXXVII. Bridford Mine in 1949 when still at work, showing headgear over shaft and conveyor belts leading to mill. It is possible that the nearer figure (bottom left hand corner) is Col. Ramsden himself. (Western Morning News).

Plate XXXVIII. Bridford Mine in 1962, four years after closure. View from shaft showing conveyor belts.

I noted that the shaft was then 280 feet deep, with intermediate levels at 80 feet (adit) and 180 feet, and was divided into three compartments, two for hoisting and one for footway (i.e. ladders). An electric pump was sited near the shaft bottom, discharging into the adit via a 6-inch pipe and the mine had its own power station with two diesels totalling 500 H.P. driving dynamos and air-compressors.

Ore went first to a jaw-crusher at the shaft head then along a conveyor belt and into the top of a hopper or bin. It was let out of the bottom of the bin as required and onto a second conveyor belt which took it to trommels for sizing, the larger material going to jig-washers and the fine stuff to six concentrating tables. An even more modern method of ore-separation known as froth flotation was also employed but this may have been introduced at a later date. At that time 50 men were employed underground and 30 at surface; although there were then only three levels underground the large number of underground miners is accounted for by the fact that the lode had many branches so that there were a corresponding number of working "ends".

Revisiting the mine in September, 1962, beyond noting that the shaft had been concreted over and the headgear and winding machinery removed there seemed to have been little change since the abandonment four years previously except that everything appeared very rusty and generally unserviceable. A certain amount of memorabilia was lying around including a calendar with pages prior to July, 1958, torn off, a scale from a pump indicator near the shaft site graduated from 0 to 900 gallons per minute and some Daily Mine Reports which showed that by 1958 a depth of 600 feet had been reached.

According to newspaper reports of the time, the site had been bought in 1960 for the sake of the scrap machinery on it but the purchaser was in trouble soon afterwards for allowing mine water to escape and pollute the River Teign, killing large numbers of fish. It should be mentioned that on the site was a considerable area of lagoons or slime ponds so one or more of these may have overflowed to cause the pollution. In 1964 I noted that the buildings and machinery were in course of being dismantled.

Further newspaper reports said that ownership passed into new hands in 1967, the purchaser making utterances about re-opening the mine, this time for lead and zinc, but such an idea did not find favour with the planning authorities. Likewise an alternative proposal to landscape the area and turn it into a caravan park was also turned down, one of the grounds for refusal being possible danger to children from the nearby slime ponds, although when I saw these in September, 1967, they were empty; this may of course have been seasonal. In the following year there were murmurings about unusual geiger counter readings near the shaft site, uranium and possible negotiations with the Ministry of Technology, but to my knowledge nothing came of this.

In 1989 the site amounted merely to an area of waste ground from which all mining machinery, buildings and other structures had been removed, the only evidence of past activity being the lagoons — dry in the aftermath of the summer's prolonged drought. The floor of the original open quarry had been cleared and grassed over and some modern sectional buildings erected on it but veins of barytes could still be seen in the quarry face and it was possible to get a view of the main site from the vicinity of the quarry.

Plate XXXIX. Bridford Mine - general view in 1962.

CHAPTER 9

BULKAMORE MINE AND ITS TRAMWAY, RATTERY 749631

ONE OF A NUMBER OF SMALL LOCAL IRON MINES which flourished for a short time in the 1870s, Bulkamore is situated in Mine Copse, just over a mile north of Rattery Church and produced 4,000 tons of brown haematite between 1874 and 1875. It is of interest mainly on account of the inclined tramway which connected it to the South Devon Railway (later G.W.R. Ashburton branch and now the Dart Valley Steam Railway) and also because it showed a brief flicker of activity as recently as 1938.

Some authorities suggest that it was previously known as Brent Mine which the official *Mineral Statistics* show as having been at work in 1865, though no production figures are given. The statistics in respect of the latter give a location of "Brent", presumably meaning South Brent, which parish does adjoin Rattery, but there seems to be an alternative possibility that, rather than having been the same mine as Bulkamore, Brent Mine may have been later re-opened as Harbourneford Mine, shown in the 1874 statistics as "Harbour Ford", Ivybridge (sic), Harbourneford being in fact two miles N.E. of South Brent and within the latter parish.

Bulkamore Mine and its tramway were researched in the 1970s by Michael Messenger, who wrote a brief history which was published in the *Industrial Railway Record* for April, 1977 and also in *Devon Historian*, but since then some further information has come to light which is included below.

Taking the mine itself first, the principal workings were within Mine Copse, where there was a substantial openwork running along its southern boundary, while beneath the centre of the copse was a large oblique excavation or stope extending about 80 feet in an easterly direction with other dimensions about 30 feet, measured parallel to the bedding plane of the rock, and about 20 feet measured at right angles to the bedding. A horizontal entrance was located on the east side of a small north-south gulley, and it was connected to surface by a vertical shaft near the inner end. In addition to these features there were three adits as marked on the accompanying sketch plan, two just inside the northern boundary of the copse and one in the field adjoining it to the north.

A visit to the mine in 1989 disclosed that the openwork was up to 30 feet deep and 20 or 30 feet wide, though various rubbish had recently been dumped in it in places, while the underground excavation, with

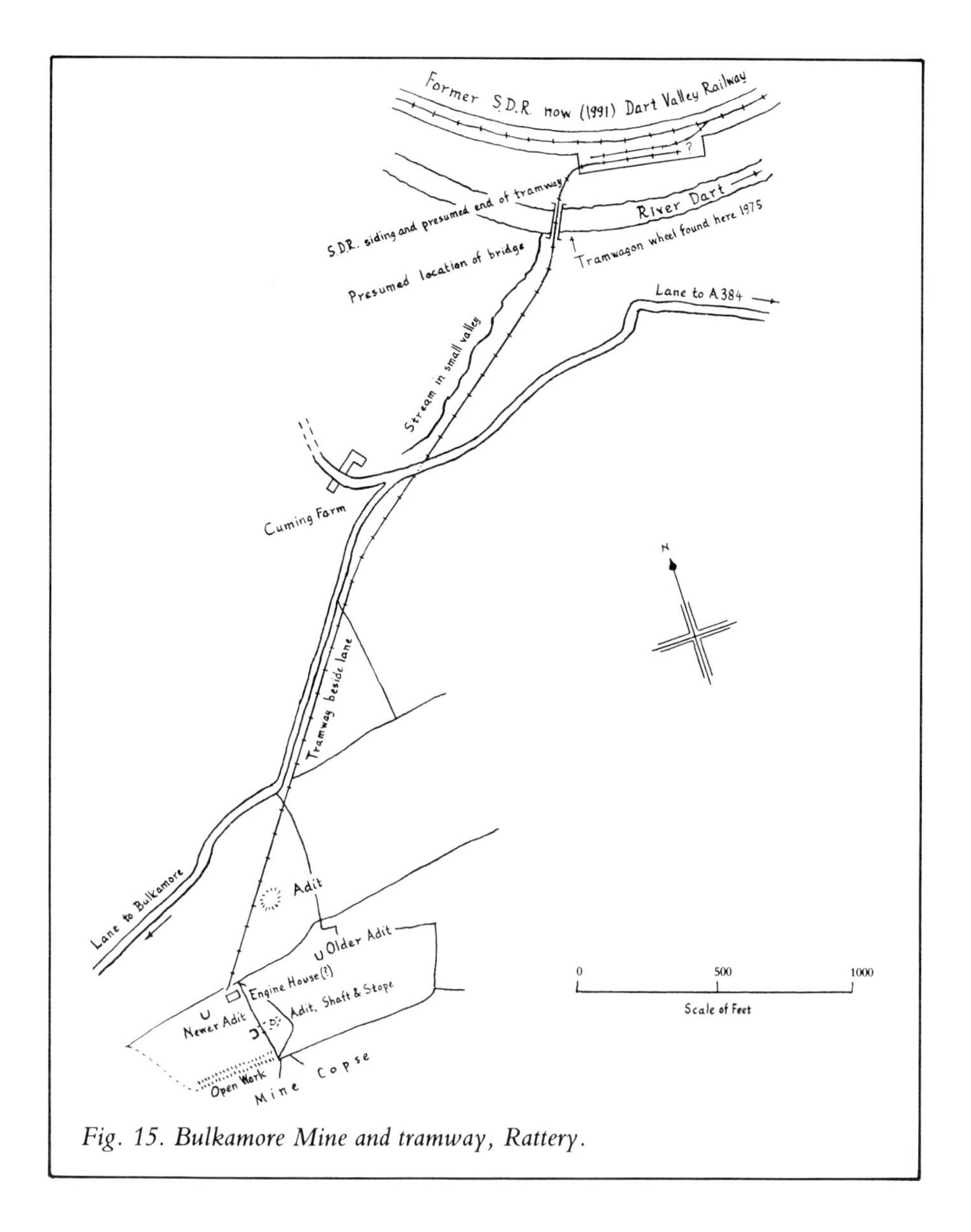

Fig. 15. Bulkamore Mine and tramway, Rattery.

shaft and horizontal entrance, was intact. Of the three adits, the position of the one in the field was marked only by a small tree-covered dump, the easterly one within the copse had a fallen and partly blocked entrance while the western one was clear, about 6' 6" high and 3' 6" wide and, being driven in compact slates, seemed likely to remain open for the foreseeable future.

It is improbable that any processing of the ore was carried out on the mine, barring perhaps some hand-picking, so that it would have been sold to the smelters virtually as excavated. Initially it had been despatched to Totnes for onward shipment by a fleet of carts but as this had proved unduly expensive the ore was diverted to the main line railway at South Brent. This too proved costly on account of the general inaccessibility of the mine by road so in view of the nearness of the S.D.R. Ashburton branch it was decided to construct an inclined tramway down to the latter, whence it could be transported to the quays at Totnes via a newly opened line branching off from the main line at Totnes Station.

Regarding the tramway, it will be seen from the sketch plan that it went initially N.N.E. from the mine down to Cuming Farm, a distance of 600 yards, in a straight line, of which 250 yards were beside the lane leading from Cuming Farm to the former Bulkamore Farm. I had originally thought that this straight stretch of the lane had formed part of the course of the tramway itself but it seems that this was not so and that the tramway ran directly beside the lane on its east side, the latter being a much older way which would have had to be kept clear for agricultural use. The upper part of the tramway was exceedingly steep and there is evidence to show that it was cable-operated and probably worked by a steam engine: the *Totnes Times* for 28th November, 1875, reported that the mine manager, Thomas Dugard, suffered, a broken leg when he was caught by a rope when machinery was being started, so it is reasonable to suppose that this was in connection with the hauling arrangements for the incline. Older Ordnance Survey maps show two small buildings at the upper end of the tramway, one of which could have housed the steam engine and winding drum.

From Cuming Farm the course of the tramway altered to N.E. and was a good deal less steep and no longer straight, running down to the River Dart along a ledge cut into the S.E. side of a small lateral valley at some height above the valley bottom, ending abruptly at a miniature cliff about 20 feet above river level. From there it must have crossed the river on some sort of timber bridge, very probably continuing across the flat meadow on the further bank on trestles to reach the S.D.R. siding. It is not known how the ore was transferred to S.D.R. wagons, but the siding was without doubt of main line (broad) gauge, so it would have been convenient for the end of the tramway to run beside it but at a higher level, so that tramwagons could be tipped or discharged direct into main line wagons. How the loaded tramwagons were moved from Cuming Farm to the S.D.R. siding is also an open question, but given adequate braking arrangements they could have continued on under gravity and been manoeuvred by hand over the level parts. For the return journey to Cuming Farm the empty wagons could have been pulled by horses and then hauled up the steep slope back to the mine by cable.

Recent visits to the area revealed no traces of the upper part of the tramway nor of the buildings at its head. Lower down, however, its course along the ledge referred to above is easily discernible from Cuming Farm to the Dart, and the fenced widening of the former S.D.R. land to accommodate their siding can easily be seen by anyone travelling on the Dart Valley railway today, but no vestige whatsoever of the bridge over the river has so far been found.

When Messenger wrote, the only known surviving piece of mechanical equipment was a cast iron tramwagon wheel which I had found in the Dart, but since then some other items have come to light, including a number of lengths of the original rails from the incline (currently in use as farm fencing) and some well preserved hardwood sleepers. The rails were of the "bridge" design, understood to have been originally developed by Brunel for his broad-gauge railway system, and were in 14½ foot lengths, while the sleepers (found in the mud of the western adit) had pairs of bolts or clenches so placed as to show that the gauge of the line had been two feet. Admittedly these presumably came from a tramroad originally laid in the adit but it seems reasonable to suppose that the incline would have been of the same gauge.

I was recently afforded a brief sight of a photograph purporting to be of the remains of one of the original four-wheeled tramwagons, a box-like and rusty item lacking one pair of wheels, but no further information about it was forthcoming. Likewise I heard from another source that an axle and pair of wheels (perhaps the missing ones) were lying about somewhere in the copse. A recent search, hampered by undergrowth, was unsuccessful but it would have been interesting to have examined the wagon, which appeared to be of the non-tipping variety, to see what facility it had for discharging its load.

Up to the time of Messenger's articles there had been no firm evidence that the tramway had ever been actually used but since then an entry in the *Totnes Times* for 18th September, 1875, has been found which reported that 561 tons of iron ore were despatched from the Bulkamore Siding to Totnes in the preceeding half year.

Regarding the later activity referred to in the first paragraph above, in 1938 I was told by an informant living in Clearbrook and versed in mining matters that Bulkamore Mine had been re-opened in June of that year and was being worked by adit by a concern known as South Devon Minerals. At that time I was about to go abroad for a period of years so had no opportunity to follow up this report, but at a much later date I was told by another equally reliable informant that though the mine had in fact been re-opened the venture had come to nothing, and it seems most unlikely ever to be worked again.

CHAPTER 10

KIT TIN MINE, SHEEPSTOR
563674

ALTHOUGH THIS MINISCULE MINE, 1/4 MILE E.S.E OF Sheepstor Church, may never have reached the stage of regular production it merits some attention if only because it possessed the basic essentials of a mining operation, albeit in miniature, most of which were still in situ well within living memory and located only yards from a public road.

Plate XL. Kit Tin Mine in 1934 showing granite wheelpit (the wheel itself had by then collapsed into it), the Cornish stamps and two of the three buddles.

The site is thought to be an old one; Lysons, writing in 1822 listed "Ringmoor Down Mine" as having been last worked in 1809 and I was told by Mr R. Hansford Worth that many years later it was re-opened as Kit Tin Mine. Additionally Wood's Map of Dartmoor, probably published in the 1850s, and not necessarily reliable in every respect, shows "Sheepstor Tin Mine" as being in roughly the same location. J.H. Collins, writing in 1871, stated that gold as well as tin was found at Sheepstor and this information has been repeated by other writers as recently as March 1991, when a *Western Morning News* feature on possible gold prospecting in Devon added the words "in significant quantities" though no actual location has ever been given.

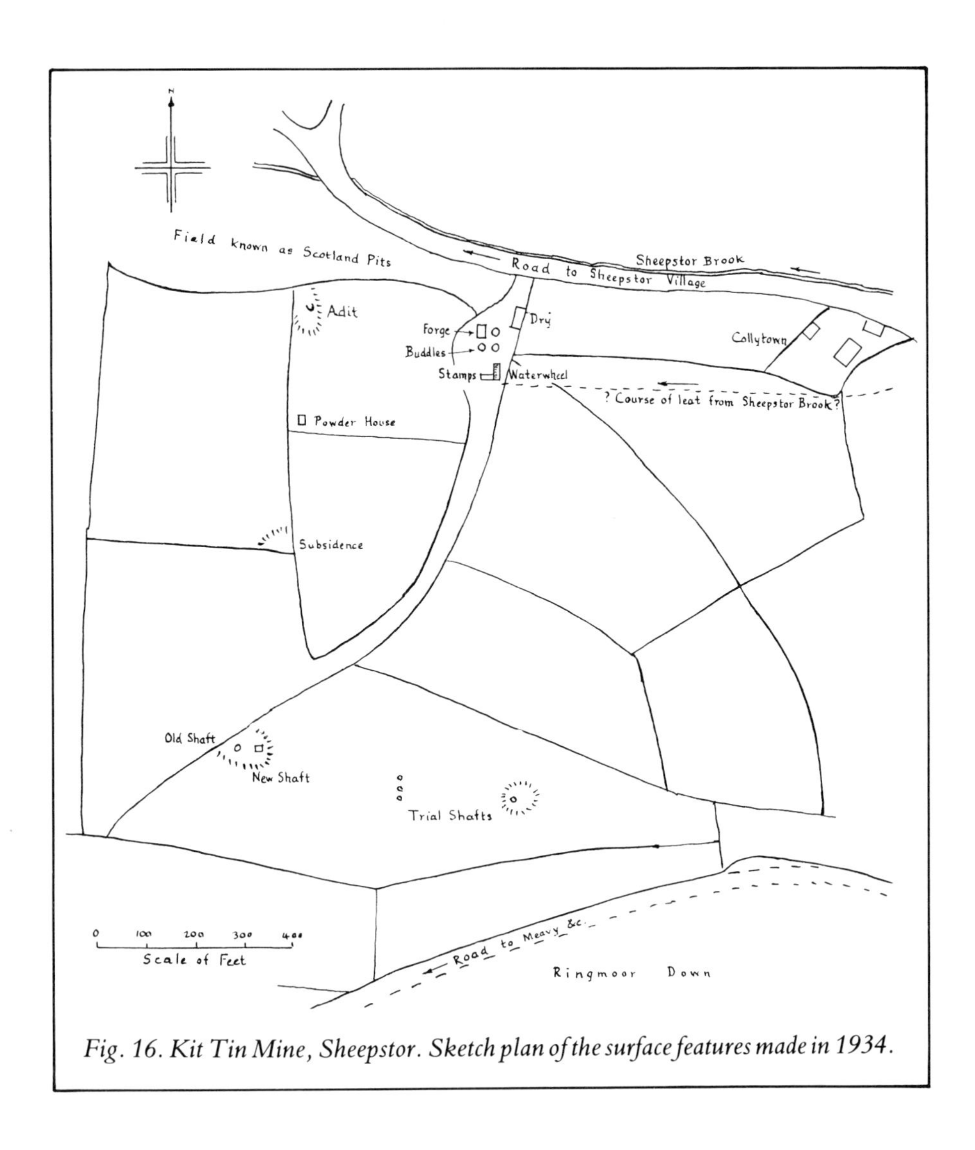

Fig. 16. Kit Tin Mine, Sheepstor. Sketch plan of the surface features made in 1934.

The first firm information about latterday operations is found in the official Lists of Mines of the U.K. which refer to an apparently unsuccessful re-opening by Kit Tin Mines Ltd., which company employed about a dozen men (half of them underground and half at surface) between 1901 and 1904, and C.F. Barclay, writing in 1925, said that it was thought that some further exploratory work was carried out in 1915/16.

The name crops up again in the Mines Lists for 1918 and 1919, when the P.F.T. Corporation of London was shown as employing three men

Plate XLI. Newer shaft at Kit Tin Mine in 1938 showing barrel of former windlass used as part of covering for shaft.

Plate XLII. Older shaft at Kit Tin Mine, 1938, with traditional iron kibble lying nearby.

clearing an adit level at Kit, though this activity apparently lapsed in 1919. The P. F. T. Corporation also had an interest in East Kit Hill Mine and Wheal Benny, both in the Stokeclimsland area, employing the same manager, J. H. Harris-James, for all three mines (one wonders how he travelled between Stokeclimsland and Sheepstor) and though work at East Kit Hill also ceased in 1919, Wheal Benny carried on until the late 1920s.

F. C. Ferguson made a detailed examination of Kit Tin Mine in 1919 and wrote a lengthy report, mentioning two shafts, one of them a new one, well timbered and equipped with ladders, kibble-way and windlass, while an adit had been driven north from a point 100 yards west of the mill area which was open to within a short distance of the older shaft.

In the mill area by the roadside was an 8-head battery of Cornish stamps driven by a waterwheel 20 feet diameter and 2 feet breast, three convex buddles worked by a smaller waterwheel, a blacksmith's shop and a building used as a "dry", while further away was a small powder house.

A similar report made by C.F. Barclay in 1925 gave the depth of the new shaft as 25 feet and its size 5 feet by 4 feet but said that the adit had by then become blocked by a rock fall 30 yards in from the entrance.

I first saw the mine in 1934 when the stamps and gearing from the larger waterwheel were more or less intact though the wheel itself had collapsed into the wheelpit. In addition the concrete bases of the buddles were in good order with their various shafting, bevel gears, etc., lying nearby while the building containing the forge was in a reasonable state though the "dry" had gone. The newer shaft was open to about 4 fathoms, timbered and having a ladderway and hand-opèrated windlass with a conventional iron kibble. The older shaft, partly filled in, must originally have been 25 or more fathoms deep.

Round about that time I was told by an elderly inhabitant of Sheepstor who had, I think, lived there all his life and who was then probably in his late seventies that 12 men were employed and that due to the large amount of incoming water the adit was driven to drain it off. Due to a miscalculation, however, the adit missed the shaft, continuing on to intersect the lode, which yielded "diamond tin", some 30 fathoms from surface. He said that the expense of driving the adit was so great and the yield of tin so small that the mine was abandoned soon after, being offered for sale for £5,000 for some time, during which an offer of £3,000 was turned down. At the time this information was given to me I was unaware that there had been two distinct periods of work since 1900 so did not inquire which period he was referring to though it seems likelier to have been the earlier one. Diamond Tin was a local term for tin ore occurring in unusually large crystals which agrees with information in

C.F. Barclay's report and the depth figure of 30 fathoms is roughly what would have been expected; thus it is reasonable to accept the other information as correct also. Concerning diamond tin, when on a visit to Kit Hill (Ch.14) in about 1940 when the dump at the mouth of the Excelsior Tunnel was being re-worked, I picked up a fragment of quartz with a large tetragonal crystal of tin ore embedded in it, at which Jennings called to Guest (or perhaps it was vice versa) "Look, he's found a tin diamond!"

By the mid-1950s the new shaft had become filled in to surface although the adit mouth was still partially open, but by the mid-1970s such is the power of modern earth-moving equipment that virtually all traces of shafts, dumps and trials in the diamond shaped field at 562672 had been obliterated and the area grassed over to become an ordinary meadow. As a further play on the word "diamond" I believe that a past mine manager there was a Captain Dymond.

The stamps, which had been such an interesting feature, were removed and sold for scrap in 1936 and though the mill area is now heavily overgrown with mature trees, the forge building and stonework of the wheelpits are in good order, with the concrete buddles easily discernible nearby. Permission to visit should be sought from the nearby Yellowmead Farm.

Plate XLIII. Kit Tin Mine; substantial masonry formerly enclosing the waterwheel, photographed in 1989.

CHAPTER 11

MINING AT DEVON GREAT CONSOLS AFTER 1913
426733 (The new arsenic works)

ANYONE VISITING THE SMALL MARKET TOWN OF Tavistock today might find it hard to believe that a mere four miles to the west and within the rural district known as Tavistock Hamlets was the fabulously productive group of copper and arsenic mines known collectively as Devon Great Consols — said in mid-Victorian times to have been the richest in Europe, their £1 shares on occasion changing hands for as much as £800 each.

Much has been written about the mine and if all the available information were put together it would fill a sizeable book, but I will make only brief reference to its main period of work, which was from 1844 to 1903 when in its heyday up to 1,300 persons were employed. The original sett contained five large mines situated along the two mile length of an enormously rich lode, the names reading from west to east being Wheal Maria, Wheal Fanny, Wheal Anna Maria, Wheal Josiah and Wheal Emma. Some other lesser mines were also opened within the sett, including one named Wheal Frementor which was about half a mile south of Wheal Anna Maria.

As explained in an earlier chapter, a typical mineral lode was originally a near-vertical fissure in the earth's surface in which minerals had been subsequently deposited by percolating solutions or vapours in past geological time. In addition to being some two miles long, the main Devon Great Consols lode was up to 40 feet wide and extended to a depth of at least 1,800 feet, the first percolations having deposited a massive layer of arsenical ore up to six feet thick on the walls of the fissure while different percolations later filled the remaining space in the centre with copper ore.

The initial discovery at Devon Great Consols in 1844, which was in a wood at what became Wheal Maria, was so sudden and the lode so rich that ore was being brought up more quickly than it could be disposed of, so had to be dumped anywhere amongst the trees. A Victorian named Chowen describing the scene wrote that the piles of ore "much more resembled heaps of gold than of the baser metal, and represented a combination of gorgeous metallic wealth and sylvan beauty the like of which would never be seen again."

Until about the 1870s the mine's wealth was derived from the copper ore taken from the centre of the lode, there having been little demand for arsenic in earlier days. But fortunately when the copper deposits began to show signs of exhaustion a demand for arsenic began to assert

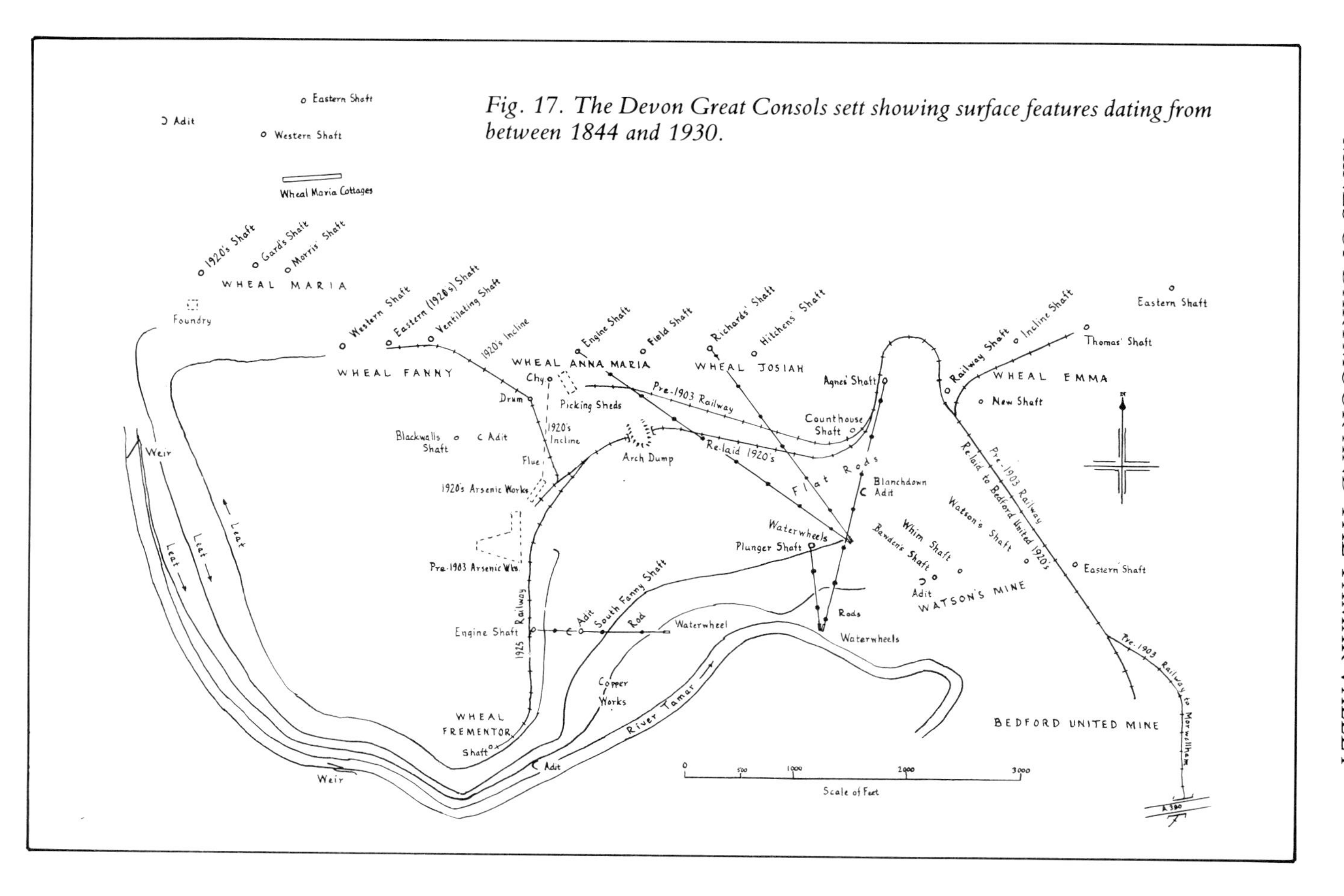

Fig. 17. The Devon Great Consols sett showing surface features dating from between 1844 and 1930.

itself — amongst other things for use as an insecticide to combat the ravages of the boll-weevil in the American cotton fields. Consequently attention was then paid to the arsenical deposits which had been left untouched on the walls of the lode, the mining of which prolonged the mine's life for a further quarter of a century, until the closure in 1903.

While copper ore was sold as such to the smelters, "white arsenic" (oxide of arsenic) was produced on the spot in the mine's own refinery, and in order to make the ensuing pages more comprehensible to the general reader it may be desirable to outline the processes employed to obtain white arsenic in its final condition ready for sale.

Initially the ore, which was a sulphide of arsenic and iron known as arsenical pyrites or "mispickel," having been crushed and if necessary dressed, (i.e. concentrated by removal of waste material) was roasted in a calciner, of which several varieties existed, the resulting arsenical fumes being led through a lengthy range of flue chambers ending at a tall stack. Within the chambers the vapour condensed into a greyish substance known as crude arsenic or arsenic soot which was then dug out and roasted a second time in a refining furnace, fumes from which were led through special chambers with clean tiled floors, on the walls and roofs of which pure arsenious oxide was deposited in clusters of dazzling white crystals. These were in turn dug out, ground to powder between millstones, packed in paper-lined barrels and sold.

Following the closure in 1903, Devon Great Consols lay almost completely idle for some twelve years, but in about 1915 underground mining was recommenced at Wheal Fanny for arsenic and at Wheal Frementor for tin and tungsten under the auspices of the Duke of Bedford who was then working the neighbouring mines of Bedford United and Ding Dong, the four together employing some 50 men at that time. Ding Dong is outside the scope of this chapter and Bedford United, which lay to the south of Wheal Emma, will only be mentioned insofar as its connection with the mines of the original Devon Great Consols sett arises.

Activity built up over the war years, reaching a peak in 1918, after which it declined until by the end of 1921 it was at a relatively low level. During those years the stamping (i.e. crushing) and mechanical concentration of ores was carried out at Bedford United while the arsenic burning was undertaken at the old Coombe Arsenic Works near Calstock. Transport between the various locations was initially by cart or lorry, but the northern end of the original Devon Great Consols railway (which had formerly linked the mine with the quays at Morwellham) was relaid as a narrow-gauge tramway between Wheal Anna Maria and Bedford towards the end of that period, the mineral wagons being hauled by a petrol-driven Simplex locomotive.

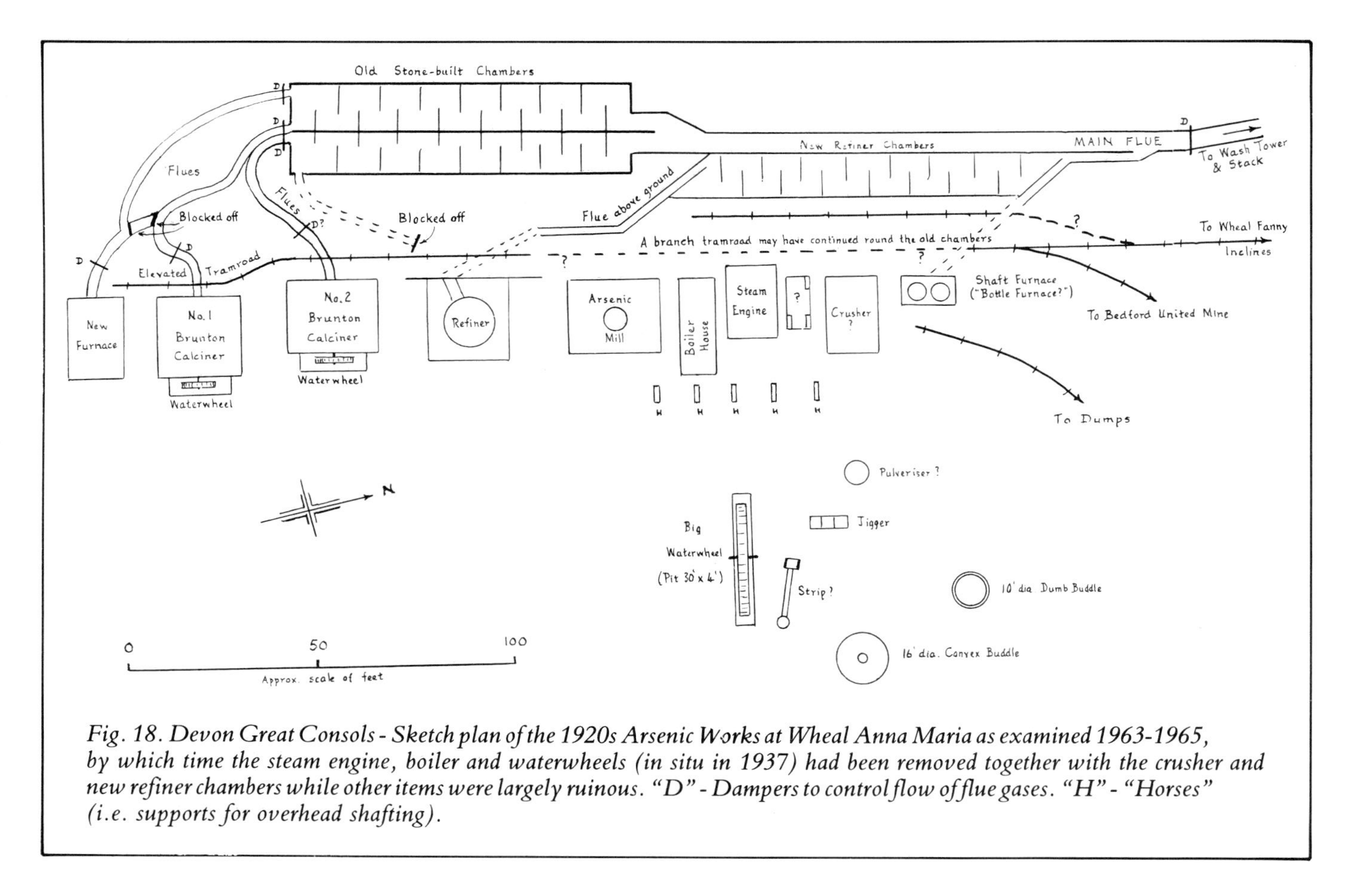

Fig. 18. Devon Great Consols - Sketch plan of the 1920s Arsenic Works at Wheal Anna Maria as examined 1963-1965, by which time the steam engine, boiler and waterwheels (in situ in 1937) had been removed together with the crusher and new refiner chambers while other items were largely ruinous. "D" - Dampers to control flow of flue gases. "H" - "Horses" (i.e. supports for overhead shafting).

Having survived the slump of 1921, which had spelt the end of some other local mines, Devon Great Consols began to prepare for a limited resurgence which was to come in the following year, and it is at that point that the evidence of the "Workbooks" referred to in the Introduction begins. These recorded daily activity between 1922 and 1925 at Wheal Maria, Wheal Frementor (which they refer to as "Framator"), Wheal Fanny (surface work only) and at a newly-constructed and smaller arsenic works at Wheal Anna Maria, sometimes referred to as "Devon Consols". Bedford United seemingly kept its own work records, which are unlikely to come to light now, while indications are that underground work at Wheal Fanny was also recorded at Bedford.

The workbooks, although now frail, sometimes stained to the point of illegibility and not an unbroken sequence, are to my mind exceedingly interesting as successive foremen made a practice of recording daily the name of each man employed and the exact duties on which he was engaged. For the first year or so the books were undated — the then foreman merely wrote down the day of the week — but on one day he was evidently absent so that the day's entries were written in by a deputy who very helpfully added the date in full, proving that the book related to January 1922, and also enabling four succeeding books to be dated.

It seems that the books were sent elsewhere weekly (apparently to Bedford United), partly because they were needed by the wages clerk but additionally for the information of "Captain", and they also served as a vehicle for small messages in both directions, these latter giving some clue to the managerial hierarchy whose names do not necessarily appear in the work lists. In transcribing from the books I am at pains to quote the exact words used as these reflect actual details of life on the mines sixty or more years ago and may include now-forgotten mining terms surviving from an even earlier era — some of the older men employed in the twenties must without doubt have worked there in the days before 1903. Such extracts will be given in quotation marks.

The amount of available detail is so great that only a minute fraction of it can be reproduced here — in the first two months alone over a hundred different activities are recorded — but studied in conjunction with contemporary photographs and with verbal information supplied since by men who worked at the mines it has been possible to build up a fair picture of what went on. It was also my good fortune to see the latterday arsenic works not many years after it had been abandoned, when almost everything was still intact — large waterwheel which had come from the manganese mill at Morwellham, steam engine and boiler, crusher, calciners and the small waterwheels which operated them, refining furnace, arsenic flues, condensing chambers and stack, and finally the arsenic mill with the last half-filled barrel of arsenic still under it.

Plate XLIV. Waterwheel at 1920s Arsenic Works at Devon Great Consols with arsenic stack beyond. Photographed 1938.

As already implied, the first book is dated January 1922, when activity was already under way, but fortunately some information about the prior and otherwise unrecorded build-up is given in a supplementary book relating to "Horse and Lorry Hire — D.G.C." which dates from September 1921, continuing forward to overlap the first workbooks and chronicling the assembly of materials (especially at the new arsenic works) for the construction of calciners, refiner, waterwheels, railroads, etc., and for the repair of existing buildings.

In January 1922, one calciner was already operating to produce crude arsenic, implying that the new stack (still standing today) had been completed, probably near the site of a pre-1903 one whose flue had seemingly been adapted to use the new stack; certainly many early entries relate to "flue repairs". Other typical items include "Extending Arsenic Shed", "Tarring Refiner Shed", "Repairing old buildings for Cooper's Shop", "Fetching elevator from Downgate Mine", "To Weir Head for tiles for refiner chambers" and "Erecting waterwheel".

At that time arsenic ore was coming from Wheal Fanny, e.g. "At Wheal Fanny, hoisting," "Repairing Wheal Fanny engine," "Changing hoisting rope, Wheal Fanny," etc. By mid-1922 we have the first mention of the building of a railway between Wheal Fanny and the arsenic works, which included cable-operated inclines to take it over the intervening higher ground, e.g. "Cutting railroad to Wheal Fanny," "Ballasting

Plate XLV. Old mining landscape Devon Great Consols 1938. Brunton calciner on left and in distance the raised launders carrying water out onto the dumps for subsequent treatment at the Copper Works.

railroad," "Making rolls for railroad," (these were flanged rollers set between the metals to support the slack of the cables — they often seized up causing the wire cable to wear deep grooves in them), "Erecting drum" and — later that year — "Working drum gear." The latter was a stationary Fordson tractor suitably modified by the addition of a winding drum to haul a train of wagons up one incline and to lower it down the other, so was sited at the highest point and its position could still be discerned in relatively recent years. The bottom of the southernmost incline linked up with the Wheal Anna Maria to Bedford United railway so that second quality ore could be sent to Bedford for stamping and returned to the Arsenic Works for further treatment, while first quality ore went direct to the Arsenic Works.

The stone-built flue chambers (still partly intact today) contained two separate labyrinths of flues and initially one set was used to condense crude arsenic and the other refined arsenic, but later in 1922 a third set of chambers was added to collect only refined arsenic, e.g. "Building flue, new refiner chambers", "Material for new refiner chambers", "New refiner chambers roof", etc.

There were by then two "Brunton" calciners and one refining furnace and a regular routine was established for each consisting of "Lighting up," "Working" and "Letting out." Working went on round the clock

Plate XLVI. 1920s arsenic condensing chambers, Devon Great Consols 1963, showing access doors. Flue to new refiner chambers is centre right and arsenic stack in distance.

for up to three or four weeks and required three men for each furnace, operating in 8-hour shifts during the week and in 12-hour shifts at week-ends to allow for time off. Corresponding entries occur for "Cleaning out arsenic soot, calciner chambers" and "Cutting down arsenic, refiner chambers". In addition, some "jiggers" were constructed — simple devices for concentrating low-grade ore — e.g. "Taking out ground for jiggers", "Attending to jiggers" and "Making new sieves for jiggers".

For the first part of 1923 work continued along similar lines except that there were some signs of shortage or impoverishment of ore, necessitating more careful treatment of what there was by provision of additional ore-dressing equipment. Entries occur for "Building buttle (buddle?), jigger floors" and "Making a strip for dressing plant", while some re-working of dumps also took place, e.g. "Estate crusher and (steam) lorry to dump" and "Carting water to dump for Garrett lorry."

In the Spring of 1923 a book is missing, leaving a 3-month gap and the story recommences in July 1923 with the first mention of Wheal Maria, e.g. "Collaring up shaft, Wheal Maria", "Erecting gin-legs", "Making shaft door", "Testing lode" and finally "Stoping" (removing ore) and "Hoisting", for which latter function the "Estate Horse" was borrowed although later on a portable steam engine was used.

At the same time work continued at Wheal Fanny with such entries as "Working Wheal Fanny hoisting gear" and "Repairing rolls, Wheal Fanny incline", but as already mentioned underground work was evidently recorded elsewhere — it is known from another source that five pairs of men were employed in the stopes at that time.

Plate XLVII. Wheal Frementor c.1925/30. Garrett engine with chain drive transferred from road wheels to hoisting drum. Driver S. Jones. (Photographer not known).

Plate XLVIII. Mineral train leaving Wheal Frementor en route for Bedford United Mine c.1925/30. On the train S. Rodda and R. Griffiths. Peeping over top of engine shed S. Jones. (Photographer not known).

Work went on at the Arsenic Works with extensive references to the building of a "New Furnace", which was completed and in use by the winter of 1923 — possibly the excessive coal consumption of the Bruntons was proving too expensive and the new furnace may have been intended as an economy measure. At the same time daily entries

Plate XLIX. Group of miners on the railroad near Wheal Frementor c.1925/30. Left to right - S. Jones, E. Honey, J.H. Higman, C. Saunders, W. Williams, W. Honey. (Photographer not known).

appear "Stoping, Wheal Maria" and "Attending to pump, Wheal Maria", together with references to continuing work at Wheal Fanny, while at the Arsenic Works the ore-dressing plant was being augmented by some more sophisticated equipment. Pumping was of course necessary when the workings were taken below the level of the water standing in the mine and initially it had been removed by means of a syphon pipe but this was only possible down to a depth of about 28 feet. Subsequently a Petter pump was installed underground with its exhaust pipe led up the shaft to surface.

By mid-1924 work was in full swing at Wheal Maria with regular daily entries of "Stoping", "Driving" (exploring for fresh ore), "Tramming", "Filling kibbles" (bucket-like containers in which ore was brought to the surface), "Hoisting" and "Landing", while by implication work continued at Wheal Fanny. Towards the end of 1924, however, there were signs of difficulties at Wheal Maria, e.g. less emphasis on "Stoping" and more on "Driving" also on the picking over of old dumps.

Unfortunately a further 3-month gap occurs at the end of 1924 and when the record recommences in January 1925 the picture had changed drastically: although arsenic production continued from dump ore ("Dressing dump ore", "Picking over Wheal Fanny dump", "Getting old rinkle", "Crushing dump ore for Bottle Furnace" etc.) underground work at Wheal Maria and Wheal Fanny had ceased and the main effort had been switched to "Framator" (Wheal Frementor) where work had been suspended since 1919. Entries occur in respect of "Moving hoisting lorry from Wheal Maria to Framator" and a major project, occupying up to half of the available work force of about 40 was "Extending railroad to Framator" from Wheal Anna Maria. At Frementor characteristic preliminaries of "Timbering shaft", "Preparing to pump", etc., are recorded, following by "Stoping", "Filling kibbles", "Hoisting" and

"Landing", then a key entry "Preparing to send in tin ore" and shortly afterwards "Sending in ore for stamps", implying that the railway was then in use between Frementor and Bedford.

The record of the workbooks regrettably ends in May 1925, which is probably the date that the Arsenic Works was abandoned, although mining at Frementor, together with limited re-working of dumps, carried on until about 1930.

In the thirties and early forties the only continuing activity was at the "Copper Works" where metallic copper was extracted from the copper-impregnated streams which flowed down through the enormous dumps of pre-1903 waste rock by precipitating it onto scrap iron — mostly old horseshoes — which activity had probably gone on since before 1903. The water was led through narrow parallel wooden launders in which the scrap iron was placed and endeavour was made to vary the courses of the streams feeding the works by leading them out onto the dumps in raised launders, whose position could be altered from time to time.

During the 1939-45 war some ochre was taken from the main drainage adit at Wheal Josiah and some ore from the dumps was sent to the mill at the nearby Prince of Wales Mine at Harrowbarrow, while in about 1949 a quantity of tailings was put through the mill at New Consols Mine, Luckett.

In about 1965 a small but relatively sophisticated modern plant was put up to treat dump ore and included a ball mill, several concentrating tables and a magnetic separator. This was operated by a succession of companies but I have no information as to how well they did and this activity had ceased by 1979.

In that same year, an international concern was said to be planning a test drilling programme to a depth of 4,000 feet (later modified to 2,600 feet) in the hope of locating the perhaps mythical deposits of tin supposed to lie beneath the original copper and arsenic deposits but the results were said to have been discouraging and nothing more seems to have been done.

In 1981 there were newspaper reports of opposition to further proposals for prospecting in the area and finally (1989) it seemed likely that the area of former dumps (some of which had been bulldozed away) would be given over to afforestation.

The whole future of mining in the upper Tamar valley has in any case been put in jeopardy very recently by the construction of a major water abstraction plant beside the river immediately above New Bridge, Gunnislake. This is designed to pump water into the Plymouth water supply network so that any attempt to re-work Bedford United, Devon Great Consols, or indeed any other upriver mine, would inevitably be resisted on the grounds of possible pollution of the water.

CHAPTER 12

DEVON GREAT CONSOLS IN THE 1920s - SMALL DETAILS 426733 (The new arsenic works)

THIS CHAPTER IS WRITTEN FOR THOSE WHO WOULD like to be taken further into the minutiae of local mining endeavour of 65 or more years ago, for whom the following snippets have been culled from the 1922-1925 Devon Great Consols workbooks referred to in the preceding chapter. These give some details of the managerial hierarchy together with specimens of messages which were passed to and fro by means of notes in the books, and a facsimile of a daily workbook entry is also appended. The names of the miners have been included to make the record more personal; some of those involved may be identified in the photographs.

Plate L. Bedford United Mine - shaft on the Main or Marquis Lode with substantial ore-bin. The miners (left to right) are B. Box, C. Moyle and F. Higman. The railway from Devon Great Consols comes in from the left of the picture, which dates from the 1920s. (Photographer not known).

As stated in Ch.11, the messages give some clues about the management, whose names do not necessarily appear in the books. From signatures, initials, etc., these appear to have been "Captain" (probably J.L. Inch, thought to have worked from Bedford United Mine), "Sam" (believed to have been Sam Pengelly, foreman until the end of 1923 and whose daughter married Jack Cloke, a local prospector and miner - see Chapter 1), "H.H." (without doubt Harry Higman, foreman from 1924; I remember him in the early 1940s when he operated the copper precipitating works at Devon Great Consols) and "Lew" (understood to have been Lew Hocking, the Wages Clerk). There was also a shadowy figure in the background named Burgess: a note dated 14.1.25 to Lew said "Burgess will send in S. Rodda's time" and in the 1930s a notice board near the stack said "Persons hauling gravel to inform Burgess, Wheal Anna Maria".

Of other messages, one written late in 1922 read "Sam - will you please find out from the six men you started this week the rates of pay they had on the Estate as Captain wants to know. Kindly send in word when you send the time book in - Lew". (The Estate would of course have been the Bedford Estate). The answer given was "Rates of pay per week - new hands - J. Burgoyne, F. Trim, J. Rich, W. Jordan, 34/- each, J. Harris, N. Braily, 32/- each". i.e. £1.70 and £1.60 respectively in today's money.

Some weeks later a note from Sam read "Book J. Rich's time for Wed. and Thur. as getting stone for hot flue". (The hot flue was a short flue between a calciner and the arsenic condensing chambers, which was being repaired at that time). The answer sent back was "I have put J. Rich's time right. You have not got J. Hookway's name for Friday and Saturday. I have booked his time to new railway - is this right?" (They were then laying the railway from Wheal Fanny to the Arsenic Works). Sam replied "Hookway's time is right - he was present".

Two further messages from late in 1922 read "S. Williams' name is not shown. I have put in his as if he was present. Please let me known if anything different - Lew". The answer given was "S. Williams was here working drum gear Monday" (for details of this see Chapter 11). I met S. Williams many years ago and he gave me some useful information about the mines.

Going on to 1923 we have a note "C. Moyle finished up after Monday night shift. C. Saunders in his place Tuesday night". (I never knew C. Moyle but believe he went abroad soon afterwards, though I did know his brother A. Moyle, another underground miner. C. Saunders was a very small man who wore a large floppy hat and smoked a large pipe).

A source of queries round about that time was the "lorry mens' time". It is not clear who they were - probably they were on Bedford United's

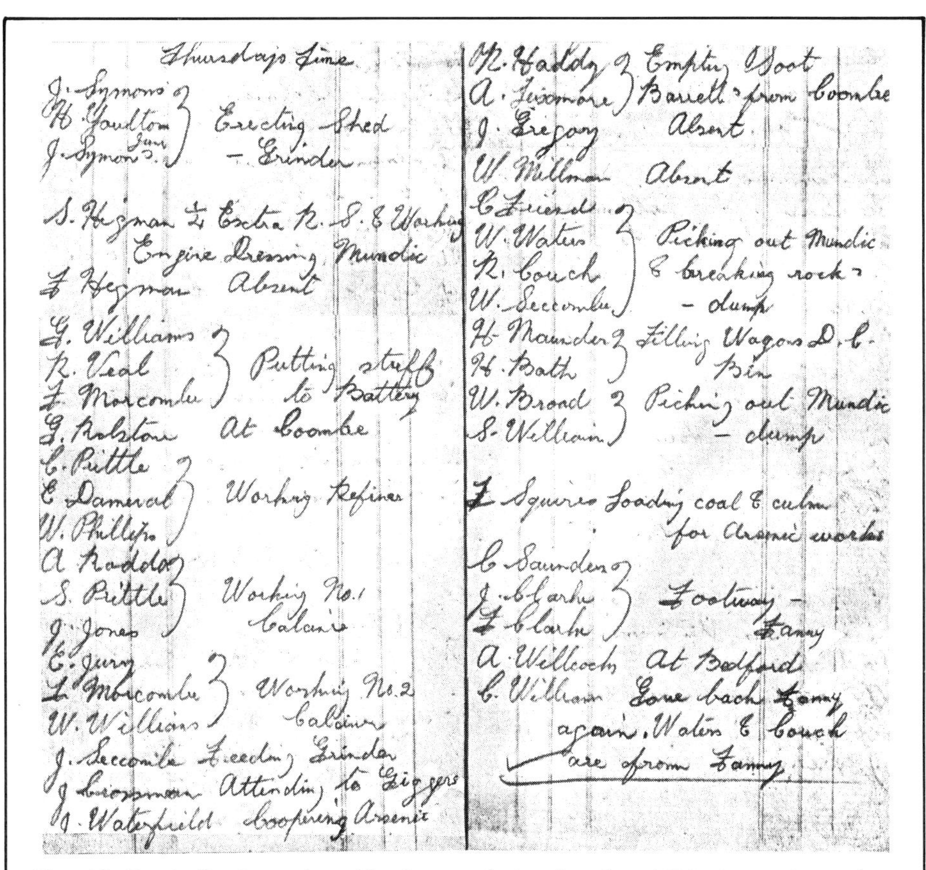

Thursday's Time

J. Symons
H. Goulton } Erecting Shed
J. Symons Jun — Grinder

S. Higman ¼ Extra R.S. & Working Engine Dressing Mundic
F. Higman Absent

G. Williams
R. Veal } Putting stuff to Battery
F. Morcombe
G. Rolston At Coombe
C. Pittle
E. Damerel } Working Refiner
W. Phillips
A. Haddox
S. Pittle } Working No. 1 Calciner
J. Jones
E. Jury
L. Morcombe } Working No. 2 Calciner
W. Williams
J. Seccombe Feeding Grinder
J. Crossman Attending to Giggers
J. Waterfield Coopering Arsenic

R. Haddy } Empty Soot
A. Livermore } Barrel from Coombe
J. Gregory Absent
W. Millman Absent
C. Friend
W. Waters } Picking out Mundic
R. Couch } & breaking rock –
W. Seccombe — dump
H. Maunder } Filling Wagons D.C.
H. Bath } Bin
W. Broad } Picking out Mundic
S. Williams } — dump

F. Squires Loading coal & culm for Arsenic works

C. Saunders
J. Clarke } Footway –
F. Clarke } Fanny
A. Willcocks At Bedford
C. Williams Gone back Fanny again. Waters & Couch are from Fanny

Fig. 19. Facsimile of actual workbook entry dating from late 1922. "R.S. & Working ..." meant "Raising Steam & Working ...", "Mundic" implied arsenical mundic or mispickel, and "D.C." stood for Devon Consols, implying Wheal Anna Maria where the 1920s arsenic works was sited.

payroll but that their work took them round the other mines also. A note to Sam said "Please manage between you the lorry mens' time when they are out that end. P.S. I have got them one day each for Wednesday and Thursday hauling arsenic to Station. If anything different for those days will you let me know? - Lew".

In mid-1924, after Harry Higman had taken over as foreman, Lew sent a note - "Harry, I see you have overlooked the three pumpmen at Wheal Maria for 17th June. I have put their time in - is this right?" (The pumpmen were G. Perkins, J. Honey and J. Richards, who did 8-hour shifts round the clock looking after the Petter pump underground. I only ever met J. Honey who in the 1960s kept an electrical shop in Gunnislake).

Round about that time there were a number of notes: "Lew - book extra shift for J. Richards stripping down shaft - Sam missed it a month ago". (Sam may have by then become underground foreman at Wheal Maria. "Stripping down shaft" may have meant straightening it - some older shafts were notoriously crooked which made hoisting difficult). Then "Lew - I have booked S. Renfree absent Monday as he was not here on Saturday and we did not know it". Followed by "Lew - will you get some rosum for me - H.H." (Presumably *resin*, used on machinery belts to prevent them slipping on the pulleys). Finally a note "41 ft timber, girth 2' 1" from Rubbytown for Wheal Maria". (Rubbytown was one of the Estate farms nearby, often mentioned in connection with the Rubbytown Leat).

The last book covers March to early May, 1925, when about 40 men were employed and I fancy that due to the 1925 arsenic slump the Arsenic Works at Wheal Maria probably closed down in about the middle of that year although mining at Frementor carried on for tin and wolfram. As the entries go right on to the last page in the final book it is reasonable to suppose that there were yet more books, but after the closure of the Arsenic Works, to which they had hitherto been returned after persual by Lew and "Captain", I suppose that they would instead have been sent back to Frementor as the only remaining centre of activity apart from Bedford United, so are hardly likely to come to light now.

When first reading through the final book I had felt that S. Williams' somewhat unusual occupation on the last recorded day of "Hauling pea and bean sticks" might have been the harbinger of impending doom for the mine but on reflection I think that these items may have been merely the by-products of cutting the railway through the woods above Frementor. Anyway I gather that he continued to be employed for some years to come and that Frementor did not finally close until about 1930.

CHAPTER 13

DRAKEWALLS MINE, GUNNISLAKE, AND THE ENTOMBMENT OF RULE AND BANT
425707

STANDING ON THE SOUTH SIDE OF THE ROAD leading from Gunnislake into Cornwall near the top of Gunnislake Hill, the ruined buildings of Drakewalls Mine are likely to be the first mining features noticed by visitors entering the county by that route. Its history has been chronicled in considerable detail by various writers, so beyond saying that it was an ancient mine, 190 fathoms deep, several times stopped and re-started, and a large producer of tin in the 1850s and 1860s, when up to 400 persons were employed, I do not propose to dwell on earlier statistical records.

I have, however, in my possession a very old notebook describing progress at the mine between 1848 and 1902, some of the information in it being sufficiently interesting to merit being quoted in detail, notwithstanding the fact that it relates to the pre-1914 period. For instance an early entry said "Oxland's New Process now in use", which was a chemical process for separating wolfram (tungsten ore) from tin ore which was difficult to achieve by traditional gravitational methods as both ores are heavy, while the magnetic separator, capable of picking out wolfram particles, had yet to be invented. Drakewalls is thought to have been one of the first mines to use the Oxland Process.

An accident which occurred underground in February, 1889, is recorded and although this has been mentioned in recent years by other writers a transcript of the entries around that date is worth reproducing. I have added some explanatory words in brackets where thought necessary.

Feb. 1 — 132 E (fathoms deep east of shaft) poor. 132 W producing 4 tons copper (ore) and (arsenical) mundic per (cubic) fm. Stoping N. in drivage of 132 W, producing 7 tons copper and mundic (per fm.).

Feb. 5 — Run of sand in back of 40 - two men entombed while letting the sand down from above, i.e. into the stope, from the surface. Rule and Bant entombed. No plans of old workings. Only two men, one Collings from Queen Mine and an old timberman named Smale appear to have any knowledge of the old workings and they suggested that the men could be reached from an old winze which had been filled up from a sollar for several fathoms below the adit. They therefore sank in the adit, not over the winze because the sollar was rotten, and drove through to the winze under the sollar. Men reached on 9th. They were at the bottom of the winze 100 feet below the drive.

Feb. 20 — Started sinking winze in 132 W.

Feb. 28 — The lode in the winze will yield 8 tons copper and mundic ores per fm..

On occasions like this it was not unusual for a poem to be written to commemorate the event - a similar one was composed following an accident at Gawton Mine, further down the Tamar, in 1899 when three men were killed by a rock fall - and I am indebted to Mr G. Rowe, formerly of Gunnislake and now living in Victoria, British Columbia, for a copy of the one written to mark the Drakewalls happening. The original, printed on a broadsheet and entitled "Rescued Alive!" has fourteen verses, five of which are reproduced here:-

I heard upon a Tuesday morn
A very solemn sound
That Rule and Bant were both entombed
Beneath a lot of ground.

The day passed by and night came on,
But still the men were there;
And if there had been only one
We thought he'd die with fear.

Inspector soon came to the mine
And underground he went,
With Captain Rodda's noble mind,
They both on good were bent.

And many hours soon passed away
When people gathered round,
To hear what the miners say
When coming from the ground.

At last the news came up, to brace,
"Both were alive and well".
A messenger was sent with haste,
The grand news to tell.

The Inspector would of course have been H.M. Inspector of Mines & Quarries, while Henry Rodda was the Mine Captain between 1889 and 1892. An apparently unsung hero of the rescue was Thomas Chapman, one of the mine agents though exactly what part he played I do not know. The ordeal was made worse by the facts that not only did the men have little food and few candles but that in addition one of them was deaf. The experience must have affected the two men profoundly but in different ways, for afterwards one became a local preacher and the other drowned himself in the river.

The record in the notebook continues for another thirteen years after 1889 although there was no noticeable production after 1895, ending on a pessimistic note in 1902. While the mine was reported as having been drained to the bottom in June, 1901, final entries in June 1902 indicate that all work except pumping had been stopped and that the shareholders had a financial crisis on their hands which was seemingly never resolved, final closure coming in 1905.

Since then there has been some minor sporadic activity above adit level; in 1918-1919 ten men were employed working over the old dumps, while I was informed by R.W. Toll that more recently a prospector named Gregson drove a cross-cut for tin in 1935 but ceased work in June of that year without any actual production having resulted.

I visited the mine in 1938 when I noted that four engine houses and six chimneys were still standing but some of these have since been demolished. At that time a shaft, probably either Engine Shaft or Matthew's Shaft, appeared to have been recently boarded over and a local elder told me that a little work had been done not long before on the east side of the working, presumably by Gregson.

At that time the Deep Adit, driven west from near the bank of the Tamar at about Grid Ref. 434707 was still open and Jennings and Guest (See Ch. 14 Excelsior Mine) who had both worked at Drakewalls offered to take me through it. This would have been an interesting experience as not only was it driven for over half a mile but various memorabilia dating from 1905 or earlier were said to have been still lying around; though I got as far as obtaining the necessary permission from the Duchy agent something or other intervened and I never made the trip, which was a pity.

J.H. Collins, who was well versed in local mining matters, writing in 1912 and referring to the 1900-1905 period, said that as the company then responsible had had to spend almost all their available money in unwatering, the amount of work done underground was trivial in the extreme and insufficient to justify condemnation of the mine. He expressed the hope that Drakewalls might be given another and better chance at some future date, but under today's conditions it is hard to see this happening for a long time to come, if ever.

Plate LI. Old engine houses and stacks, Drakewalls Mine, 1941.

CHAPTER 14

CAPTAIN MOOR AND THE EXCELSIOR MINE, KIT HILL 381724

THE EXCELSIOR SETT AT ONE TIME EMBRACED much of the Kit Hill area, just over a mile N.E. of Callington, but the name later came to be more closely associated with the Excelsior Tunnel, sometimes known at Kit Hill Tunnel.

As is fairly well known, the tunnel was driven S.S.W. from an entrance in Deerpark Wood with the intention of intersecting the North Engine Shaft of Kit Hill Mine (situated near the stack at the summit of the hill) at a point 110 fathoms below the surface. The benefits were to have been two-fold — firstly draining the workings round the shaft and secondly proving the ¾ mile of ground along the length of the tunnel where there were thought to be a number of east-west tin or copper lodes. Work began in about 1880 but was abandoned a few years later, probably due to shortage of funds, when only half way to North Engine Shaft. It does seem, however, that had the promoters opted for a smaller tunnel instead of the rather grandiose one measuring some 8 feet by 8 feet in section they could have got further.

Seemingly the area on the north side of the hill was inactive for the next three or four decades then work was resumed on a small scale under the auspices of Captain Moor. Cresacre George Moor, M.A.(Cantab), F.R.I.C., F.C.S., etc., to give his full name and quality, was born, I would guess, in about 1865 and was the author of *Tin Mining* and of *The Recognition of Minerals*. He was a chemist of some standing and was at one time County Analyst for one of the south west counties — Dorset, possibly — but I do not know how he got into mining. He was certainly at Golden Dagger Mine in 1913, then served in the Army as a captain in World War I and may have found the rank a useful handle to his name when he returned to mining circles after the war. His name first cropped up at Kit Hill in 1921, when between then and 1925 he employed up to half a dozen men working for tin and wolfram on the N.E. flank of the hill. After 1925 work ceased for a while but recommenced in the late 1930s, this time in the Excelsior Tunnel. An air compressor for working rock drills was installed near the entrance, with an air line to the working face 350 fathoms in, while there were hand-operated fan machines and their associated trunking to provide fresh air and to clear smoke from the tunnel after blasting. A single line tramroad ran the length of the tunnel (double near the working face) but this was probably a relic of an earlier epoch. Captain Moor continued the tunnel southward for a short distance at a reduced size but it was then abandoned and attention

Plate LII. Using monitor to re-work old dump near entrance to Excelsior Tunnel, c.1940. C. Jennings (left) and G. Guest (right).

Plate LIII. The author in the Excelsior Tunnel 1943. Although the tunnel was largely unsupported, timbering was necessary in places. (H.H.B. Oswell).

Plate LIV. The vicinity of the Excelsior Tunnel during underground tests in 1960. Upper picture - on the left the tunnel entrance and top right (with skylights) Captain Moor's cottage. Lower picture - tunnel entrance with air trunking installed for the tests. (Western Morning News).

switched to the dump area near the entrance. Here two old miners named Jennings and Guest (the first named having been foreman at Wheal Benny — see also Chs. 10 and 16) together with a youth (whose name I never learnt as he was only ever referred to as "the boy") were employed picking over the old dumps, principally for the wolfram which had been ignored by earlier generations, and also in sluicing out sand and gravel using a monitor supplied from a reservoir higher up the valley. Coarse material washed out from the interior of the dumps was treated in a simple jigger, fines were passed over a strip and waste rock and tailings were trammed away to a spoil dump a little way further down the valley.

At that time Captain Moor himself lived in a one-roomed cottage near the tunnel entrance under somewhat primitive conditions, which contrasted with his personal manner, which was refined — one might almost say courtly. The interior of the cottage presented an unusual spectacle: on the left, as one entered, a blazing wood fire together with his limited cooking utensils; wide shelves round the remaining walls on which was set out an array of sophisticated chemical equipment including a laboratory balance in a glass-fronted mahogany case; and in the centre and dominating the scene a large bed heavily decorated with tarnished brass rods and knobs.

The dump area near the tunnel entrance was worked out by 1941 and a small shaft was then sunk at the southern end of the wood at Grid Ref. 379723 which yielded some wolfram. By 1942 the plant in the vicinity of the cottage had been augmented by the addition of a waterwheel, a small crusher, a trommel, two sluice boxes and a dumb buddle, while a place had been prepared for two conventional circular buddles. Whether all this equipment was ever actually brought into use I am not sure, though without doubt several tons of wolfram were recovered and sent either to Hemerdon or to the Prince of Wales mill at Harrowbarrow.

The scene of operations then shifted again, this time back to the original area on the N.E. side of Kit Hill between the then Gunnislake to Callington railway and the summit, but activity there seems to have dwindled and by 1946 all mining had ceased.

A visit to the site in 1954 showed it to be deserted and the cottage empty, but the shaft at 379723 had been deepened and there was a noticeable spoil heap near it. I was later told that this shaft had been developed by New Consols Mine, Luckett, a mile or so to the north, in the late forties or early fifties, ore from it having been taken to their mill for treatment — see Ch. 15.

Since then no further mining has taken place, but in 1959/60 the Excelsior Tunnel was in the news when it was used by the Atomic Energy Authority for experiments in connection with the detection of shock waves from underground explosions. According to newspaper reports, a hut containing numerous instruments was erected at the tunnel mouth, 2,000 feet of narrow-gauge tramway was laid (sic) in the tunnel for an electric train carrying further instruments to run on, while giant extractors were used to clear the tunnel of smoke from the explosions. Several photographs were published, including one showing the tunnel entrance, Captain Moor's cottage, several portable huts and new air trunking leading out of the entrance to a presumed extractor fan a few yards up the hillside to the N.W. Narrow-gauge railway lines could be seen leading into the tunnel but these had the appearance of being the ones I remember from Captain Moor's time. This activity was only temporary, ceasing early in 1960, and I believe that the next project was to dam the entrance and use the tunnel as a supplementary reservoir to supply water to local villages but apparently nothing came of this idea.

A visit in 1989 showed the area to be so overgrown as to be almost impassable. The cottage was a ruin with roof fallen in, though the original fireplace was clearly identifiable, but the tunnel mouth, being of substantial masonry construction with an arched roof, seemed likely to last for a long time to come. It was just possible to walk along the top of the spoil heap — now overgrown with trees — and its size suggested that it was composed mainly of material derived from the original driving of the tunnel in the 1880s. But even with these features still recognisable it was hard to reconcile the scene of silent abandonment with my memories of it as it was half a century ago.

Plate LV. Looking out towards the entrance of the Excelsior Tunnel in 1966. The arched masonry lining continues in for a short distance after which the tunnel is in close granite needing only occasional support. (F.L. Booker).

CHAPTER 15

WHEAL MARTHA OR NEW CONSOLS MINE, LUCKETT 388737

A LARGE AND FAIRLY OLD MINE, KNOWN TO HAVE been at work as far back as 1838 and notable in more recent years, firstly, for its lack of success in relation to the enormous amount of capital put into it and, secondly, for the astonishing array of traditional machinery which stood there undisturbed from the time of its abandonment in the 1870s until it was most regrettably broken up for scrap late in 1938. Four engine houses (two of which are reasonably intact today) contained machinery for pumping, winding, crushing and stamping, while a 36-head battery of Cornish stamps also survived until 1938.

The mine is situated immediately west of Luckett on either side of the valley of a stream which flows east through the village to join the Tamar. The shafts are on the north side of the valley, the Engine shaft reaching a depth of about 100 fathoms on an east-west lode, and the ore-processing plant was at the bottom of the valley and on its southern side.

Originally called Wheal Martha, the name was successively changed to Great Wheal Martha and to New Wheal Martha, such name changes being a standard ploy in those times to encourage more speculators to invest in local mines. Later, for the same reason, and on the notion that the Wheal Martha lodes could be extensions of those of the neighbouring and unbelievably rich Devon Great Consols Mine, the name was further changed to New Great Consols, subsequently shortened to New Consols. In earlier years the mine was worked mainly for copper, reaching a depth of 64 fathoms in 1861, 86 in 1864 and 96 in 1870. The copper ore had to an extent been subject to troublesome contamination from arsenic accompanying it, for which there had formerly been little use, but by the end of the 1860s, when the workings had reached greater depths, tin ore was encountered and at the same time the commercial demand for arsenic increased sharply. Additionally it was found that the complex ores then being worked also contained silver and even, in minute quantities, gold.

Accordingly, the treatment arrangements were altered at great expense to deal with the recovery of these other substances using what J.H. Collins, writing in 1912, described as a combined mechanical (i.e. traditional) and chemical (i.e. newer) means. A number of calcining furnaces were erected, together with the flues and condensing chambers needed to recover the arsenic, and the vats required in connection with

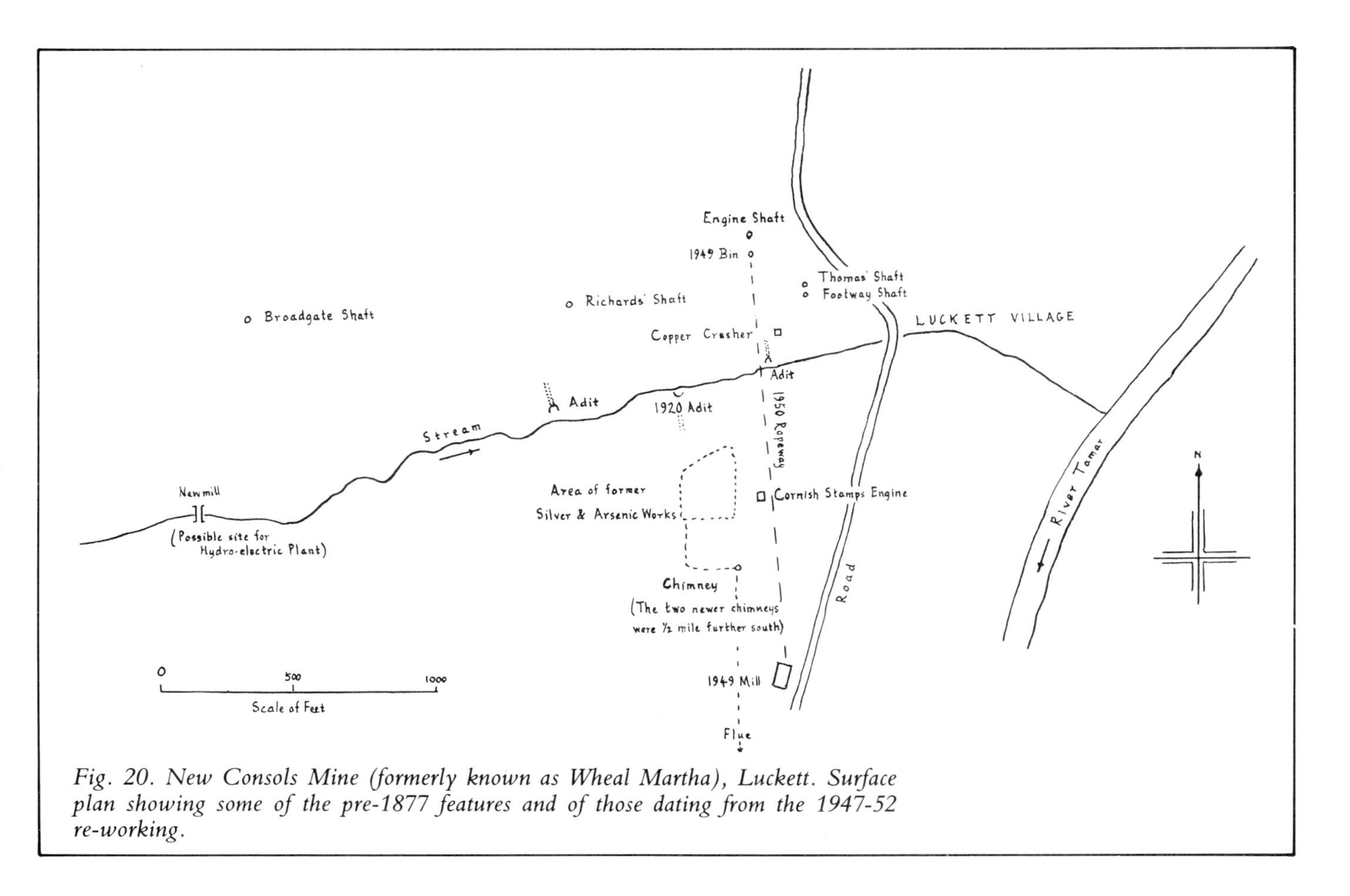

Fig. 20. New Consols Mine (formerly known as Wheal Martha), Luckett. Surface plan showing some of the pre-1877 features and of those dating from the 1947-52 re-working.

Plate LVI. Wheal Martha, or New Consols, 1929. On left is Engine Shaft and pumping engine, in centre the crusher engine and on the right the whim engine at Thomas' Shaft (H.G. Ordish).

the chemical processes were also provided. It seems that the Cornish stamps were put up on the southern side of the valley at about the same time to deal with the tin, arsenic, etc., ores, while the copper ores raised in earlier days would have been crushed in Cornish rolls worked by the engine at the bottom of the valley.

The new concern was referred to as *New Consols Silver & Arsenic Works* but unhappily for the management troubles ensued. On the one hand, the proximity of the arsenic stacks to the village gave rise to complaints about the poisonous fumes so vociferous that two new stacks had to be built nearly half a mile further up the hillside to the south and the flues extended to them — no doubt a costly business — and on the other hand, the chemical processes did not prove as successful or as economical as had been hoped. In principle such processes are understood to have involved roasting pulverised ore with some other cheap and easily available substance such as washing soda or common salt which would combine with selected constituents of the ore, insoluble in their natural state, to form soluble salts of those constituents which could be washed out and recovered separately.⋆ As a result, the mine was shut down in 1877 and the whole concern went into liquidation in about 1879 leaving heavy debts.

⋆*A process termed lixiviation (Ed)*

Plate LVII. Wheal Martha or New Consols. Steam whim at Thomas' Shaft, 1936. The winding drum has been partly dismantled exposing the chain on it. (H.G. Ordish).

Plate LVIII. Wheal Martha or New Consols. Stamps engine and stamps 1929. It is understood that the subsidiary beam worked a pump for recycling water for ore-dressing. (H.G. Ordish).

Due to the urgent need for British mineral production in the years of the Great War, some re-working of dumps and prospecting by adit recommenced in 1914 and continued until 1920, when 30 people were employed. Mechanical concentration of ore seems to have been carried out on the spot — I remember seeing a 20-head battery of Californian stamps there in fair order in 1940 — but the arsenical ore was probably sent elsewhere for burning — perhaps to the old Coombe Arsenic Works near Calstock.

The site lay idle for the ensuing quarter of a century then, in 1946, a fresh company, *New Consols Mines Ltd.*, was registered and leased the property from the Duchy of Cornwall. This company began the actual work of re-opening the following year, when the unwatering of the mine was started using electric submersible pumps. As successive levels were unwatered they were cleared of ochre deposits, decayed timbering was made good (though in the main the levels were unsupported), tramroads laid, and compressed air pipes fixed, while at surface a timber headgear was erected over the Engine Shaft and an electric hoist installed.

Plate LIX. Wheal Martha or New Consols. Cornish boiler for pumping engine, 1929. (H.G. Ordish).

At the same time a new mill, designed to deal with up to 30,000 tons of ore a year, was erected on the south side of the valley at 387733, but due to the difficulty of obtaining new machinery most of the plant in the mill had to be bought secondhand, much of it coming from the nearby Prince of Wales Mine which had closed at the end of the 1939-45 war. Primary crushing was carried out at the shaft head after which it was stockpiled in a large circular bin sited just south of the shaft. Initially ore was taken from the bin to the mill by lorry but later an aerial ropeway was constructed to join the two sites which, when I saw it in 1950, was almost complete. The mill machinery included a battery of Californian stamps of 1,250 lbs each, concentrating tables and flotation cells, all electrically driven, and was officially started up on 2nd September, 1949.

Initially, electric power for all purposes was provided by generators driven by two large diesel engines — one Paxman, one Mirlees — positioned near the Engine shaft and there were plans to set up a hydro-electric station embodying alternators driven by two turbines. It does not appear that the latter project was ever proceeded with and in 1950 electric power was being obtained from the National Grid, with the diesels kept in reserve.

Plate LX. Wheal Martha or New Consols. Valve gear and cylinder head of pumping engine in 1929. (H.G. Ordish).

Plate LXI. Wheal Martha or New Consols. Cylinder head of Cornish engine showing the rods of the parallel motion, 1929. (H.G. Ordish).

Plate LXII. Wheal Martha or New Consols. Pumping machinery at Engine Shaft in course of being dismantled in 1938. (Western Morning News).

By the end of 1949, when some 150 men were employed, including 50 underground, the mine had been unwatered to the 74 fathom level below adit and sampling had revealed the presence of workable quantities of copper, tin, silver and tungsten though it appears that at that time the management were only interested in recovering tin and tungsten. There were various set-backs in the following year, however, with pumping difficulties aggravated by heavy rains in February, also failures and breakages of mill machinery, especially the stamps. Additionally, only one cage was in use in the shaft, meaning that it was not counterbalanced so putting a heavy strain on the winding engine.

At about that time I was in fairly frequent touch with Mr. R.W. Toll of Bere Alston and Major B. Llewellyn of Hawkmoor House, Devon Great Consols, both of whom were actively involved with the mine and kept me informed of various developments. Concerning the pumping arrangements, I was told that two submersible pumps were placed in the lower levels, discharging into a reservoir in the 40 fathom level, from which the water was pumped up to adit level by a third pump. Incoming water was normally about 450 gallons per minute but in heavy rain this could increase to 700 g.p.m. or more against maximum pumping capacity of 750 g.p.m. On 7th February, Major Llewellyn wrote "I have been very busy these last few days with pumping set-backs due to heavy rain resulting in drowned levels. I am pleased to say things are better at the moment and we have got our emergency submersible pump going today so that the water is going down again..."

Later that month I was taken underground to the 64 fathom level by Major Llewellyn — a most interesting experience, not least the descent down the ancient Engine Shaft. This measured 11 ft. x 7 ft. one half of which was in use for the cage which took us down while the other half was still occupied by the pre-1877 pump rod and the 20 inch bore iron pump columns up which water had formerly been pumped. I did have one anxious moment: as we were about to enter the cage at surface, carrying unlit acetylene lamps, Major Llewellyn said something to the engineman which sounded like "We won't bother with any bells" — these being the standard means of communication from underground to the winder. As the cage descended into darkness Major Llewellyn suddenly asked if I had a match to which I, with visions of being stranded in total darkness nearly 400 feet below ground, apparently cut off from communication with the surface, had to reply "No, I don't smoke." However, my recollection is that when we reached the 64 someone waiting there for the cage obligingly lit our lamps for us.

Walking east along various branches of the level I noted that water was flowing ankle-deep everywhere and that smoke from blasting was hanging about. The water was exceedingly corrosive, necessitating frequent renewals of air and water pipes, and anti-fouling composition was being tried in order to combat this. Wood, in contrast, was pickled by it and much of the pre-1877 timbering was still sound and in use. In the prevailing semi-darkness the actual lode was not as spectacular as I had expected and not all that easy to distinguish from the surrounding country rock. There had been some roof-falls at that level, one I saw having left a vast dome-shaped cavity.

From the 64 we went up to the 40, but whether we went up in the cage or climbed the ladders I cannot now remember. That level was electrically lit and I was able to see the 100 h.p. electric pump which delivered the water up to adit level, and the final ascent back to the surface was in the cage.

Round about that time Major Llewellyn had written "I am usually at the mine six days a week — we've not long started our mill up and it's a critical period with frequent visits from our London directors..." It seems, however, that he became disenchanted with these "frequent visits," often regarding them as interference by non-mining men, and in April, 1950, told me that he had "finished up with the mine" so that thereafter I was dependent on Toll for information.

By that date, according to the latter, the mine had been "forked to bottom" (i.e. completely unwatered) and they were driving east at the 96 with the intention of getting underneath the former mineral ground which had been stoped away in the upper levels in the previous century. A hopeful pointer was the presence in the 64 East of tongues of granite in the slate rock, in which the level was driven, which were presumed to originate in the nearby granite mass — I saw one of these which was about six inches thick — and comparisons were being drawn with the most famous of all West Country mines Dolcoath, at Camborne. At Dolcoath, the mine's earlier wealth was derived from copper found in the shallower levels which were in slate, but when the copper showed signs of exhaustion the management were persuaded to sink deeper, so reaching the underlying granite where tin deposits of almost equal richness were found.

The main lode at New Consols was of considerable size, its width varying from a few feet to as many as fifteen. Other lodes were also intersected both to the north and south of the main lode, one of which was, according to Toll, 400 feet north of the main lode, while in the other direction he made reference to a "New South Crosscut." An interesting feature in the floor of the 96 West on the main lode was a hot spring issuing at a temperature of 80°F, suggesting that the lode channel was very deep and letting water up from much further underground.

In 1951, the mill was in full operation and returns of tin ore were

Plate LXIII. New Consols Mine. Machine drill in 64 fathom level West, c1950. (R.W. Toll).

Plate LXIV. Headgear at the Engine Shaft, New Consols, in 1949. The placing of a broomstick at the top was an old Cornish custom intended to ward off evil spirits. (Western Morning News).

being made, but despite the amount of work done, the money spent and all the favourable signs, it was evident by 1952 that things were not going as well as had been hoped and underground work was abandoned at the end of that year, after producing a total of 170 tons of black tin and a small amount of wolfram. The mill was kept working for a further 18 months on ore from some other local mines including, according to Toll, Wheal Arthur, East Calstock and Kit Hill, but by September, 1954 it had ceased to operate and was in course of being dismantled.

We are indebted to Mr. H.G. Ordish for the photographs he took in 1929-36, some of which are reproduced here, and it is my regret that I never saw the pre-1877 machinery myself — due solely to the fact that I did not learn of its existence in time. I am also grateful to Mr. F.L. Booker for letting me have a copy of the photograph he took in 1966 giving a comprehensive view of the site.

Plate LXV. New Consols Mine, general view taken from immediately south of the Engine Shaft, looking south, in 1966. In foreground the 1949 ore bin and loading end of ropeway, with crusher engine house just beyond it. In middle distance the stamps engine house and beyond it, near skyline, the site of the 1949 mill. (F.L. Booker).

In 1968 an older (1870s) winding engine house and its chimney at Thomas's Shaft were demolished by an individual who evidently had no feeling for the value of the site as an industrial monument and who seemingly did not even make any use of that part of the site after he had cleared it.

In 1983 there was talk of reclaiming the area for car parking and in 1985 an application is said to have been made to remove 100,000 tons of dump material for treatment elsewhere and to tidy up the place generally but nothing further seems to have come of either of these projects.

I revisited the mine briefly in 1989 and noted that the massive engine houses originally containing the pumping machinery at the Engine Shaft and the engine for the copper crusher were still in fair repair and roofed, the former being characterised by its curious gables. Everything was greatly overgrown, even when compared with 1966, and in addition to the loss of the winding engine house at Thomas's Shaft, the former stamps engine house on the south side of the valley could no longer be seen. The position of the 1949-54 mill was marked only by concrete foundations for stamps, tables, etc. Half a mile to the south was the lone survivor of the pair of 1870s arsenic stacks, though it was originally a good deal taller. When I first saw it in about 1938, not then knowing the story behind it, I wondered what its function had been, standing there on its own.

It is a pity that the final re-working, in which great hopes had been placed, was so unsuccessful; it is said that £400,000 was put into the mine — quite big money in those days — but that the amount realised from sales of ore was only £100,000. It has also been said that the failure did much to undermine the confidence of investors who might otherwise have put money into Cornish mining in subsequent years.

CHAPTER 16

SOME OTHER LOCAL MINES WORKED OR EXAMINED SINCE 1913

THIS CHAPTER GIVES BRIEF DETAILS OF OTHER MINES in the area which have either shown activity since 1913 or in which interest has been shown since that date. The list has been divided in two, the first section containing details of mines which were actually worked, or at least prospected, and the second section locations which were merely professionally examined. Almost all the mines named had been worked previously, mostly in the 19th Century, and regarding examinations the majority of these were carried out by C.F. Barclay, R.W. Toll and their associates (qualified mining men with practical experience in the district) between about 1916 and 1940. For these the abbreviation "B.T." is used and their detailed findings are recorded in the MSS referred to frequently by H.G. Dines in his 1956 Memoir. The original manuscripts are held in the Redruth Public Library, while there is a full set of copies in the Plymouth Central Library, Local Studies Department. Results of examinations by other bodies are not known but were presumably unfavourable.

For brevity, customary symbols have been used to denote the various minerals worked, viz. Ag - silver, As - arsenic, Ba - barium, Cu - copper, Fe - iron, Mn - manganese, Pb - lead, Sn - tin, U - uranium and W - tungsten and are generally based on past records so do not necessarily represent the minerals in which later miners or prospectors may have been interested.

Other mines in the area which were either worked or at least prospected after 1913.

Wheal Arthur Calstock Sn W As 434700

¼ mile S.W. of Whimple Farm. Active 1914-20 - in 1918 the main adit (50 fms below surface at Engine Shaft) was being re-opened and there were two shafts in use with ladderways and a steam hoist. Again at work in 1925 but stopped in 1926. Finally re-worked above adit only by Cookes in 1954, ore going to New Consols for treatment.

Ashburton Umber Ashburton Umber 762704

150 yds. N. of Ashburton Cottage Hospital. Active 1915 and again 1942-44. In latter years consisted of an open pit about 20 feet deep from which umber was dug out by a primitive power-operated crane and trammed to a drying furnace near the main road.

Lady Ashburton Callington W 368702

1/4 mile S.E. of Florence Park Farm. Prospected by adit 1942 but work discontinued 1943.

Baggator Petertavy Sn 550810

Immediately N.E. of Baggator Farm. In 1925 alluvial material was being washed out by a monitor, using water from a nearby leat.

Bedford Consols Tavistock Hamlets Sn As 457695

3/8 mile W.S.W. of Orestocks. Worked on small scale about 1922-23 hoisting by horse, the arsenical ore going to Devon Great Consols for burning.

Bedford United Tavistock Hamlets Sn W As 441726

5/8 mile E.N.E. of New Bridge, Gunnislake. Active 1914-30, for a time in conjunction with Devon Great Consols and Ding Dong. Employed up to 80 or so men and worked to 10 fms. below deep adit level (42 fms below surface at Engine Shaft) with aid of small Cornish pump which was still in situ in 1938. Arsenical ore went to Devon Great Consols for burning while ore from D.G.C. was stamped at Bedford United, the two mines being joined by a 2-foot gauge tramway. In about 1978 some interest in the mine was shown by South West Consolidated Minerals. See also Chs. 11 and 12.

Wheal Benny Calstock Sn W As 397731

300 yards N. of Latchley Plain Farm. Worked 1914-24 then "caretakers only" 1925-28 and abandoned Dec. 1928.

Lady Bertha Buckland Monachorum Sn As 471689

On E. bank of Tavy 300 yards N. of Balstone. Dumps worked 1915-16 and ore treated at Tavy Consols. Re-examined B.T. 1919 and 1923.

Birch Tor & Vitifer North Bovey Sn 680810

1/2 mile E. of the Warren Inn, Postbridge. Worked intermittently 1915-28 and sampled 1930 by Birch Tor Alluvials.

Blogsters South Hill Sn 345707

Immediately S. of Whitley Farm and adjoining Glen Adit. See also under Redmoor and West Redmoor.

Bowden Common Brentor Mn Ochre 464819

1/8 mile N. of Whitstone Farm. See under Whitstone Ochre. Known also as East Chillaton.

Plate LXVI. Mill at Gunnislake Clitters Mine, probably taken in the early 1900s. (Photographer not known).

Brookwood Buckfastleigh Fluorspar 718675

600 yards S. of Hawson Court. It has been reported that in the 1970s an attempt was made to re-work the Brookwood dumps for fluorspar but was not pursued due to contamination of the fluorspar by copper ore.

Calstock & Danescombe Calstock Sn As W 426695

330 yards E.N.E. of Trehill House, in Danescombe & Consolidated Tamar sett. Prospected about 1915 but not re-started. Sampled 1939. The winding engine house and other buildings have been restored by Landmark Trust.

East Calstock Calstock Sn W 426696

5/8 mile N.N.E. of Cotehele House. Examined by Ministry of Supply 1942 but it was decided to develop Ding Dong instead. Active 1954, ore going to New Consols mill.

Chillaton & Hogstor Milton Abbot Mn Ochre 432814

1/4 mile S. of Chillaton village. Open ochre pit 25 feet square and 15 feet deep, with windlass and kibble, seen 1950 when it appeared that it could have been worked in previous 20 or so years.

East Chillaton Brentor Mn Ochre 465819

1/2 mile N. of Westcott Farm. See under Whitstone Ochre. Known also as Bowden Common.

South Crebor	Tavistock Hamlets	As	465714

Between the track of the old Southern Railway and the Tavy, immediately N.E. of Lazy Bench Hill Bridge. See under New East Wheal Russell.

Crowndale	Tavistock Hamlets	Sn As	469725

¼ mile W. of Crowndale Cottage, immediately W. of track of old Southern Railway. Some work done above adit by Toll 1923-26.

Danescombe & Consolidated Tamar	Calstock	Sn As W	422695

330 yards E.N.E. of Trehill House. Active 1915 but abandoned in February of that year.

Dimson	Calstock	Sn W	427718

½ mile S.W. of New Bridge, Gunnislake. Some work done by Carter 1914-15 and by Moyse 1935. Probably little or no production.

Ding Dong	Tavistock Hamlets	Sn W	437718

⅛ mile S. of Hatchwood. Operated with Bedford United in 1920s. About 50 men employed by Ministry of Supply in 1939-45 war, mostly above adit, but a shaft with headgear was seen in 1944. Some ore treated at Prince of Wales mill. See also under Bedford United. Results generally disappointing.

Downgate	Stokeclimsland	Sn W	365731

¼ mile S.W. of South Coombe. Worked 1914-19 producing some low grade tin concentrates. Sampled 1942.

Duchy Great Consols	Calstock	As	409733

⅛ mile S. of centre of Latchley village. Tried for arsenic 1918-20 but probably no production.

Little Duke	Tavistock Hamlets	Sn As	471695

⅜ mile S.W. of confluence of Tavy and Walkham. Worked above adit with Tavy Consols 1914-20 and 1923-24.

Wheal Florence	Callington	W	364706

⅜ mile W. of Claremont. Featured in Mines Lists 1915 and 1930 when it was marked "idle" but some prospecting by adit carried out 1942.

Ford	South Tawton	As	643935

¼ mile S. of Sticklepath village. Some work carried out by Buchan 1917-20. A shaft was open to about 30 feet in 1969.

Plate LXVII. Hingston Downs Mine, probably c.1905-1915. Left foreground - Bailey's Shaft. In centre distance - Morris' Engine House which is still standing today. (Photographer not known).

Gawton Tavistock Hamlets Sn Cu As 452689

¼ mile N.W. of Great Gawton Farm. Copper precipitating by J. Cloke about 1912-26. Dumps sampled 1918-20. Attention paid to the mine 1942 but not followed up. Application made 1967 to re-process dumps and possibly work by adit, but nothing further heard.

Glen Adit South Hill Sn 345707

In about 1934 the company then working Redmoor Mine drove an adit E.N.E. from an entrance 130 yards S. of Whitley Farm and on the same lode as in the adjoining Blogsters Mine, the latter's adit having been driven in the opposite direction, i.e. W.S.W.

Gooseford South Tawton As 672925

½ mile N.W. of Higher Gooseford and also known as West Gooseford or Throwleigh. Stopped 1914, examined B.T. c. 1916, re-opened 1918 and worked until 1924 then on care & maintenance basis 1925. Steam power known to have been employed and a pulsometer possibly used for pumping. The dumps had been cleared away and removed by 1972.

Gunnislake Clitters Calstock Sn W As 422724

¼ mile N.W. of North Dimson. See under Kit Hill, Gunnislake Clitters & Hingston Down.

Hawkmoor Calstock As Cu Sn W 435726

¼ mile N.E. of New Bridge, Gunnislake, and inside the sharp bend of the Tamar. Knott worked to about 10 fms below adit with aid of a steam pump about 1912-20 and produced small quantities of these ores from underground and from dumps. An application to prospect was made in 1972 but no more heard.

Haye South Callington (?) Sn (?) 341690 (?)

Possibly ½ mile S.E. of Trevigro. See under Redmoor.

Haytor Iron Ilsington Fe 773771

Immeditately S. of Shotts. Worked 1916-21.

Plate LXVIII. Watson's Shaft at Prince of Wales Mine, possibly dating from about the turn of the century. In addition to the engine house and pump beam the picture shows the cantilever arrangement for the balance box and the shear legs for raising and lowering heavy items in the shaft. (Photographer not known).

Hemerdon Plympton St Mary W 572587

On N. side of Hemerdon Ball, worked on a large scale 1914-20, examined 1928 and worked again on an increasing scale 1936-44 though not very successfully, mostly by opencast, material being transported to the mill by an aerial ropeway. The plant was retained on a care & maintenance basis for some years after the closure and in 1952 the mine was "expected to re-start shortly," but this did not happen. The ropeway was demolished in February, 1961 and all plant removed, so that by 1964 the mill building was an empty shell. Interest in re-opening was again shown in 1965 and since that date the mine has been the subject of innumerable newspaper reports with the mining company Amax wishing to re-open and conservationists in opposition. In 1986 approval was given for mining to re-commence, subject to certain environmental conditions, but since then nothing has been heard - presumably due to the fall in metal prices.

Hingston Down Calstock Sn W As 410714

1/4 mile S. of Hingston Down Quarry. In 1981 Brampton Resources applied for permission to explore. See also Kit Hill, Gunnislake Clitters & Hingston Down.

Holditch Marytavy As 509801 (?)

Apparently worked briefly in 1923. No details known.

Holmbush Stokeclimsland As 360720

1/4 mile N. of centre of Kelly Bray village. Dumps worked over about 1919 and was active in part in about 1922.

Kingswood Buckfastleigh U 713665

Prospected 1918-20 when an adit was driven north from beside the stream flowing east through King's Wood from Bowerdon and presence of pitchblende reported. The discovery received enthusiastic acclaim in the local press at the time but was dismissed later as probably of little commercial significance. Said to have been investigated in the 1939-45 war and in 1949 a newspaper report said that it was to be developed as a model mine where geologists could be trained in the detection of radioactive minerals. A similar report in 1967 brought the matter to notice again, this time in connection with the detection and measurement of radon gas, which in turn was very much in the news in 1989-91 regarding its being a health hazard in granite areas.

The adit was still open in 1980 but should not be entered on account of high levels of radioactivity.

Plate LXIX. An undated photograph which could possibly have been taken in about 1914 and is inscribed "Counthouse Shaft, Redmoor." There were in fact two Counthouse Shafts - Old and New - and it seems likely that the shaft in the foreground is the old one and the more distant shaft the new one. Both are about 330 yards S.W. of Kelly Bray Sawmills and the view is over Kelly Bray village with the stack at the summit of Kit Hill on the skyline. (Photographer not known).

Kit Hill, Gunnislake Clitters & Hingston Down	Stokeclimsland and Calstock	Sn W As	375713

On and around Kit Hill and Hingston Down also at Gunnislake Clitters ¼ mile N.W. of North Dimson. Large scale mining, employing nearly 200 men between 1915 and 1920, which ceased in September, 1920, ore from the first two mines being conveyed to the mill at Clitters by means of an aerial ropeway. Small scale mining continued at Kit Hill until 1950 (see Ch. 14) while some re-working of dumps took place at Clitters in about 1944, the material being treated on the spot using simple equipment. Some test drilling in the area was reported in 1968-69.

East Kit Hill	Stokeclimsland	Sn W	389711

Immediately N. of Sevenstones. Some small scale prospecting and dump picking 1916-19. In 1981 it was reported that Brampton Resources wished to explore.

Latchley Consols	Calstock	As	409733

1/8 mile S. of centre of Latchley village, on part of the old Duchy Great Consols sett, and worked in conjunction with Wheal Williams and Great Wheal Williams between 1917 and 1920.

Longstone Bridge	Bickington	Sn	792715

In the 1960s some alluvial tin ore was removed from the valley of the Kestor Brook upstream from Gale, near Longstone Bridge, by Western Alluvials Ltd. for treatment elsewhere. It was further reported that minute quantities of gold were associated with the tin ore but that the amounts were so small as to be commercially valueless. Round about the same time there were reports of possible similar activity elsewhere in the area, including the valley of the Ashburn between Ashburton and Buckfastleigh, but these appear to have come to nothing.

Owlacombe & Stormsdown	Ashburton	Sn As	770733

1/2 mile N.E. of Owlacombe Cross. Worked 1914-20 and again in 1925. Dumps re-worked for tin about 1937 and again, by Roskudda, in about 1958, traces of the latter's activity being still discernible in 1962.

Pride of the East	South Hill	Sn	345707

Immediately S. of Whitley Farm. See under West Redmoor.

Prince of Wales	Calstock	Sn	401705

1/4 mile S.S.W. of Mount Pleasant. Active 1914-15 but stopped February, 1916. Examined about 1928 but not re-started. Some activity about 1938-49 — a small but up to date plant was installed 1940. Latterly only the mill was kept working, treating ore from other local mines, including Devon Great Consols; earlier on some ore from Ding Dong had also been treated here. In about 1971 a Canadian company carried out exploratory work including drilling but this ceased in 1974. In the early 1980s Brampton Resources showed interest in the mine.

West Prince of Wales	Calstock	Sn	389707

1/4 mile S. of Sevenstones Farm. Active 1914-15 but abandoned in October, 1915.

Quither	Milton Abbot	Mn	441812

Immediately W. and N.W. of Quither Farm and active in 1924. Some minor work was carried out in 1937 and several tons of ore were extracted in 1942. The underground workings were still open in 1952.

Redmoor	South Hill	Sn W As	356710

1/4 mile S.W. of Kelly Bray. Re-opened 1917 and worked until 1920 during which time New Shaft, North Shaft and adit to North Shaft were cleared, the shafts timbered and a mill together with Brunton calciner and chambers built. Again worked 1930-38 and a new mill put up but was idle when visited in January, 1939, having latterly been operated in conjunction with Glen Adit. Listed as active during the war years 1940-45. In 1978 Consolidated Goldfields given permission to prospect by drilling. Finally, in 1980-82 South West Consolidated Minerals expressed interest in Redmoor together with Blogsters and Haye South. They established temporary offices, set up drilling rigs and applied for planning permission for a substantial mine, but since the collapse of tin prices nothing more has been heard about this.

West Redmoor | South Hill | Sn | 345707

Immediately S. of Whitley Farm. Unsuccessful attempts to re-open and unwater were made in 1928, 1934 and 1938. Known also as Pride of the East and as Blogsters.

Roborough Down Wolfram | Bickleigh | W | 525648

¼ mile W.N.W. of Lower Goodameavy. Active on a very small scale between about 1938 and 1942, ore being sent to Hemerdon for treatment. Some further interest was shown in the site in 1952 but this appears to have come to nothing.

New East Wheal Russell | Tavistock Hamlets | As | 465714

Opened and prospected for arsenic 1922-23 but not actually re-worked. Known also as South Crebor.

Shaugh Iron Mine | Shaugh Prior | Fe | 532632

¼mile N.W. of Nethershaugh. Attempts to re-open by adit made by Ward in 1938 but came to nothing. Sampled by Ministry of Supply 1943.

Silver Valley | Calstock | Sn W | 384702

¼ mile N.W. of West Harrowbarrow. Prospected 1917-20. Some work done by in 1938 by Stedman who installed a small plant. Re-opened in 1943 by Ministry of Supply and more elaborate plant put in, together with pumping and hoisting gear, but closed before end of war. In 1977 S.W. Consolidated Minerals given permission to research the mine but nothing more heard.

Sortridge Consols | Whitchurch | As | 510708

⅜ mile N.E. of Bedford Bridge. Dumps picked over 1924 and mine re-examined B.T. 1928. Some material from dumps said to have been used in construction of R.A.F. Harrowbeer in 1939-45 war.

Stormsdown	Ashburton	Sn As	767731

Examined B.T. 1928-30. See under Owlacombe & Stormsdown.

Tavy Consols	Tavistock Hamlets	Sn Cu As	469688

¼ mile S.E. of Hocklake Farm. Worked with Little Duke 1914-24, treatment of ore from both mines being carried out at Tavy Consols.

Throwleigh	South Tawton	As	672925

See under Gooseford.

East Vitifer	North Bovey	Sn	708823

⅛ mile S.W. of West Coombe Farm. Work suspended from 1915.

Whitstone Ochre	Brentor	Ochre	464818

Immediately W. of Whitstone Farm. The nearby area included Bowden Common (or East Chillaton) as well as Whitstone. Active in 1942. Some ochre pits were noted in the area in 1968.

Wheal Williams and Great Wheal Williams	Calstock	As	408738

¼ mile N. of centre of Latchley village. See under Latchley Consols.

Mines in the area which were professionally examined after 1913 without being actually worked or prospected.

Anderton	Whitchurch	Sn	485723	B.T. 1918/30
Battishill Down	Bridestowe	Ag-Pb	521863	B.T. 1921
Bottle Hill	Plympton St Mary	Sn Cu As	563587	B.T. 1919/28
Burley Wood	Bridestowe	Not Known	495875 (?)	Rio Tinto 1982
Crebor (Canal Tunnel)	Tavistock Hamlets	Cu As	459722	B.T. 1923/33
West Crebor	Tavistock Hamlets	Cu	450719	B.T. 1922
Devon & Courtenay	Whitchurch	Cu Pb	472717	B.T. 1919/21
West Down	Tavistock Hamlets	Cu	487707	B.T. 1920/21
Emily (See Ramsley)	S. Tawton	Cu	650930	B.T. 1916/20
Wheal Exmouth	Christow	Ag-Pb	838830	Black Rock Ventures 1982
Frank Mills	Christow	Ag-Pb Ba	836820	B.T. 1920s Black Rock Ventures 1982
Furzehill Wood	Walkhampton	Sn As	516692	B.T. 1924/31
Wheal George or East Wheal George	Walkhampton	Sn Cu	529704	B.T. 1918/19
North Hooe	Bere Ferrers	Ag-Pb	427661	B.T. 1919
Huckworthy Bridge	Walkhampton	Cu	532707	B.T. 1918/19
Hemerdon Consols	Plympton St. Mary	Sn	565579	B.T. 1928

Ivybridge Consols	Ivybridge	Ag-Pb	648550	B.T. 1923
Maristow and Lopwell	Bere Ferrers	Ag-Pb	471648 & 474653	B.T. 1923
Wheal Mary Hutchings	Plympton St. Mary	Sn As	564581	B.T. 1928
Martin's Farm (vicinity of)	Drewsteignton	Not Known	685929 (vicinity of)	Amax 1980
Ramsley (with Emily)	S. Tawton	Cu	650930	B.T. 1916/20
East Wheal Robert	Whitchurch	Cu	518707	B.T. 1918/19
North Wheal Robert	Whitchurch	Sn Cu	513708	B.T. 1924
North Roborough Down	Buckland Monachorum	Sn	513684	B.T. 1932
Wheal Russell or Russell United	Tavistock Hamlets	Cu	438711	B.T. 1922
East Wheal Russell	Tavistock Hamlets	Cu	450710	B.T. 1922/33
Great West Sortridge Consols	Whitchurch	Sn Cu	496707	B.T. 1923
Sourton Tors (vicinity of)	Sourton	Not Known	Possibly 537892	Consolidated Goldfields 1966
Wheal Sydney	Plympton	Sn As	551593	B.T. 1923
Virtuous Lady	Buckland Monachorum	Sn Cu	473698	B.T. 1920/21
Walkham & Poldice	Buckland Monachorum	Sn Cu	490708	B.T. 1917/36
Walkham United	Buckland Monachorum	Sn Cu	493704	B.T. 1917/36
Week	Milton Abbot	Mn	457806	Sir A. Russell 1944
Great Week	Chagford	Sn	713875	B.T. 1931
William & Mary	Tavistock Hamlets	Cu	463702	B.T. 1922/23
Yeoland Consols	Buckland Monachorum	Sn	518663	B.T. 1930
South Yeoland	Buckland Monachorum	Sn	511659	B.T. 1930

Plate LXX. Engine house and stack at West Crebor Mine, photographed in 1938, but which regrettably have now been demolished.

CHAPTER 17

CONCLUSION

WITH METAL MINING IN DEVON COMING TO AN end over twenty years ago and with the last surviving Cornish mines closing down in 1991 it is hard to speculate on which, if any, of the ore-processing methods and devices described in preceding chapters would be used in the event of a mining revival in the South West. Assuming that any future mine would have to be a large one if it were to be viable at all, it seems that to keep wage bills within bounds the accent would have to be on efficiency and on self-acting appliances and, with present day fuel costs, on the avoidance of processes involving heat.

Ore from underground would still have to undergo some primary sizing and crushing involving tradition grizzlies and rock-breakers but stamps are unlikely ever to be used again in the West Country, having been replaced by gyratory crushers such as rod mills and ball mills some 30 years ago. Screens were still in use in 1991 for sorting intermediate sized particles but by then upward-current cone-type classifiers had been replaced by cyclones for sizing small particles.

Buddles and kieves survived until the mid-1960s although mines then using them would probably have modernised sooner had they been able to afford to. By today's standards these would be too slow and too labour-intensive, although effective in their way. Continuous-acting jiggers still have a place in modern mills, however.

Frue vanners went out of use due to their limited capacity, which meant that large numbers of them had to be employed, with a correspondingly adverse effect on wage costs, but concentrating tables are still very much in use world-wide and likely to remain so.

Magnetic separators are also still in current use where required and include the older belt-type ones although alternative designs have since been developed.

Calciners continued to be used in Cornwall until the early 1960s after which they were replaced by modern flotation systems. The latter not only cut out the heavy fuel bills entailed in calcining but also the cost of working and maintaining the furnaces themselves with their attendant ranges of flues, chambers and stacks.

In contrast to all the above changes it is perhaps surprising to note that, as well as being used by prospectors, vanning shovels still have a place in modern mills for checking and sampling. A senior mining consultant recently told me "There is nothing to beat them!"

Plate LXXI. Ramsley Mine, possibly in about 1910. (Photographer not known).

Plate LXXII. Ramsley Mine in 1967. The chimney, the masonry structure at the shaft head and the track of the incline are still discernible.

GLOSSARY

(Not exhaustive. Explanations are limited to those needed to support the text)

ADIT
Horizontal entrance into mine, sometimes called a day level, its main purpose being to drain water from the workings.

ANGLE BOB
See Turnbob.

ARCHIMEDEAN SCREW
See Auger.

ARSENIC
This term normally refers to oxide of arsenic and may be crude arsenic or arsenic soot (impure) or refined or white arsenic (99% pure As_2O_3). See Ch. 11.

ARSENIC ORE
See Mispickel.

AUGER or Archimedean Screw
Device for propelling thick slurry along or up a conduit.

BALANCE BOX
Counterpoise to take part of the weight of the pump rod in a shaft.

BALL MILL
Device for reducing ore to small particles. See Ch. 2.

BARYTES
Barium sulphate, $BaSO_4$, principal barium ore.

BATTERY
Set of stamps which could comprise as few as two individual stamps to as many as 64 or more.

BEAM
See Rocker Bob.

BEAM PUMP
See Cornish Pump.

BIN
See Ore Bin.

BLACK TIN
Oxide of tin, SnO_2, the end product of the ore-dressing processes in a tin mine.

BOB
See Rocker Bob.

BOILER
Usually either Cornish (horizontal with single fire tube extending along its length) or Lancashire (two parallel fire tubes side by side).

BOTTLE FURNACE
A small shaft furnace similar to a limekiln, used for arsenic burning in the early days of the industry. Such a furnace existed at Devon Great Consols (Ch. 11) but is something of an enigma as it was built as recently as 1924 and its flue leads directly into the main flue to the stack without going through the arsenic-condensing chambers.

BRIDGE
Low partition between fire and hearth in reverberatory furnace. See Ch. 6.

BRIDGE RAILS
Tramroad rails whose section resembled an inverted letter U with exaggerated outer serifs.

BRUNTON CALCINER
See Calciner.

BUDDLE
Simple circular and square buddles have been described in Ch. 2, while in a circular concave buddle the pulped ore was fed in at the circumference and flowed inwards towards the centre. Other developments also existed — See Rack Frames and Round Frames.

BURNING HOUSE
Old term for building where ore was calcined or "burnt". See also under Calciner.

CAGE or Skip
Box-like container which could be raised or lowered in shaft to convey men, ore, etc. Usually ran in guides termed cage (or skip) roads.

CALCINER
A furnace in which ore was roasted either to drive off unwanted constituents or to sublimate them for separate recovery or to render the ore more amenable to subsequent processes. Could be an ordinary reverberatory furnace as described in Chs. 5 and 6 or a Brunton calciner as referred to in Chs. 4, 5 and 11. The latter type had a slowly revolving circular bed played on by flames from peripheral furnaces. Ore was fed onto the centre and automatically raked towards the circumference as calcining proceeded until it fell into a cooling chamber below. Other varieties existed. See also Bottle Furnace.

CALIFORNIAN STAMPS
See Stamps.

CAPTAIN
Mine superintendent or manager.

CASSITERITE
Tin dioxide, SnO_2, the principal tin ore.

CHAMBERS
See Condensing Chambers.

CHIMMING
Final stage in the concentrating of tin ore. See Ch. 2.

CLASSIFIER
Device for sizing very small ore-particles in which pulped ore was fed into the top of a downward-pointing cone against an upward-flowing current of water, fine particles being carried up and overflowing from the top of the cone, coarser particles overcoming the current and falling to the bottom where they could be drawn off through a spigot.

COLLAR
See Shaft Collar.

CONCENTRATE
Ore which has been freed of waste.

CONCENTRATING TABLE or Shaking Table
Usually a rectangular table about 16 feet long and 6 feet wide given a special vibrating motion which caused particles on it to progress along its length while a stream of water tended to wash them across the table. But along its length were many low parallel strips or riffles of diminishing heights over which the lighter material was washed while the heavier particles stayed between the riffles to reach the end of the table. Many varieties existed under various trade names — Wilfley, James, Record etc.

CONDENSING CHAMBERS
A labyrinth of connecting compartments in a flue in which arsenical vapour was condensed into either crude or refined arsenic. See Ch. 11.

"CONSOLS"
Abbreviation of "Consolidated" and a common suffix to mine names, intended to inspire confidence in prospective investors.

COPPER ORE
Many varieties exist but the most common locally was Copper Pyrites, a sulphide of copper and iron, $CuFeS_2$.

COPPER PRECIPITATING
Achieved by leading copper-impregnated mine water over scrap iron on which metallic copper was deposited for subsequent recovery. See Ch. 11.

CORNISH ENGINE
Typically a single-cylinder steam engine with its piston rod pointing upwards and connected to one end of a pivotted beam, the other end of which could be connected to pump rods in a shaft if a rise and fall motion was required or to a crank if rotary motion was called for. Cylinders could be of enormous size — up to 90 inches or more in diameter while steam pressure was low by modern standards — usually round about 40 p.s.i. See also Parallel Motion.

CORNISH PUMP or Beam Pump
A simple force-pump sited at shaft bottom and connected to a power source at surface by a vertical rod, water being forced up to the surface or to adit level through a rising main or "pump column". See also Cornish Engine and Balance Box.

CORNISH ROLLS
See Rolls.

CORNISH STAMPS
See Stamps.

CRIB
A packed meal eaten at the mine.

CROSS COURSE
A vein, usually non-metalliferous, making an obtuse angle with adjacent lodes.

CROSSCUT
A level driven at an obtuse angle to the lode(s) in a mine.

CRUDE ARSENIC
See Arsenic.

CRUSHER
Or Jaw-crusher or Rock Breaker. Device as commonly used in quarries for reducing relatively large pieces of ore to roadstone size.

CULM
A mixture of anthracite and coke used for firing calciners.

CYCLONE
Modern equivalent of a cone-type classifier, involving a swirling motion of its contents.

DIPPER WHEEL
See Raft Wheel.

DRESSING FLOORS
Areas where ore was treated.

DRIVE
A horizontal tunnel, the excavating of such a tunnel being referred to as Driving.

D.O.E.
Department of the Environment.

DRY
Miners' changing house with facilities for drying wet clothing.

DRYING FURNACE
For drying ore, as opposed to calcining it. See Chs. 2 & 7.

ELEVATOR
See Raft Wheel.

END
The end of a drive or crosscut.

FLAT RODS
Horizontal wood or metal rods for transmitting power a distance by means of a to-and-fro motion.

FLOORS
See Dressing Floors.

FLOTATION or Froth Flotation
A modern method of ore-separation which relies on the fact that if air bubbles are introduced into a mixture of water and pulped ore some minerals will adhere to the bubbles and be carried up to the surface while others will not and will therefore sink to the bottom.

FLUE DOORS
Access openings in flues, especially arsenic flues.

FOOTWAY
Ladders leading down a shaft, or may imply the shaft itself.

FORK, FORKED
A reference to pumping, i.e. "Forked to bottom" meaning all water pumped out of the mine.

FRICTION HOIST
Machine for pulling tramwagons up an incline. See Ch. 5.

FROTH FLOTATION
See Flotation.

FRUE VANNER
A fairly modern ore-separating device consisting of a wide rubber belt stretched between two slowly-revolving rollers, the upper surface moving in a slightly uphill direction with a stream of water flowing down it. Pulped material was fed onto the belt, heavier ore particles surviving the flow of water to reach the top, lighter waste being washed to the bottom. Fell into disuse mainly due to limited capacity.

GALENA
Lead sulphide, PbS, and the principal lead ore. Usually contained a small proportion of silver, when it was termed silver-lead.

GANGUE
Non-metallic waste rock accompanying the ore in a lode.

GAS ENGINE
Internal combustion engine running on gas often produced on the spot. See also Producer Gas.

GEIGER COUNTER
Instrument for measuring radio-activity.

GIN LEGS
Simple headgear over a shaft.

GRINDER
See Pulveriser.

GRIZZLEY
Simple device for sizing rough ore, consisting of a sloping grill of iron bars onto which the ore was tipped, pieces which failed to fall through being passed to a rock-breaker for further reduction.

HAEMATITE
An oxide of iron, Fe_2O_3, a commonly worked iron ore.

HAMMER MILL
A modern gyratory rock breaker.

HEADBOX
A small reservoir at the point where water from a leat was passed into a pipeline leading down to a turbine or pelton wheel, built to prevent air getting into the pipeline and to intercept sand, gravel and other debris.

HEADGEAR
Timber or steel frame over shaft carrying pulleys for winding ropes.

HEADS
The richer product from an ore-dressing device, as opposed to the poorer product, the "tails" or "tailings".

HOIST
See Whim.

HOLMAN'S STAMPS
See Stamps.

HOT FLUE
A short flue between a calciner and arsenic condensing chambers, too hot for deposition of arsenic but in which flue dust was intercepted.

HUNTINGDON MILL
A type of rotary pulveriser in which rollers were spun round against an outer casing by centrifugal force, crushing any ore within the casing.

INCLINE
Sloping tramway, usually cable-operated.

INCLINED PLANE
A shaft sunk at a relatively flat angle, with a tramroad leading down it.

IRON ORE
See Haematite.

JAW-CRUSHER
See Crusher.

JIGGER or Jig or Jig Washer
Device in which gravel-sized material was formerly shaken up and down in a sieve under water, heavy ore forming a layer at the bottom with lighter waste above it. In later versions the sieve stayed still while the water pulsated up and down and the device was also made to be continuous-acting.

KIBBLE
Barrel-shaped iron bucket for hoisting ore up shaft.

KIEVE
Wooden tub, sometimes called a chimming kieve, used in final stage of tin ore dressing. See Ch. 2.

KNOCKER HEADS
Mechanical hammers for striking chimming kieves to aid settlement of concentrate. See Ch. 2.

LAGOON
See Slime Pond.

LANDING
Receiving kibbles of ore at the shaft head.

LAUNDER
Open wooden conduit for taking water to a waterwheel or carrying pulverised ore in suspension from one ore-dressing device to another.

LEAD ORE
See Galena.

LEAT
Open watercourse for conducting water across country from river to waterwheel, etc.

LEVEL
Horizontal tunnel in mine not extending to the open air.

LOADING
Masonry or concrete support for a heavy machine, e.g. a set of stamps.

LODE
A vein containing a proportion of mineral ore which had to be freed from the waste rock accompanying it. See Chs. 2 and 11.

MACHINE DRILL
See Rock Drill.

MAGNETIC SEPARATOR
Electrical device for separating magnetic from non-magnetic ore. See Ch. 2.

MANGANESE ORE
See Pyrolusite.

MILL
General term for building housing stamps, ore-dressing machinery, etc.

MISPICKEL
Arsenical iron pyrites, FeAsS, the principal arsenic ore in the district.

MONITOR
Powerful jet of water for washing out alluvial ore.

MUNDIC
Iron Pyrites, or iron sulphide, FeS_2.

OCHRE
Earthy haematite used in manufacture of yellow or brown paint.

OIL ENGINE
Internal combustion engine running on light oil such as paraffin which

was vapourised in a "vapour chamber" before being ignited in the cylinder.

OPEN WORK
A quarry-like excavation along the line of a lode.

ORE BIN
A large container for stockpiling ore prior to feeding it to the stamps, etc.

ORE DRESSING
Processing ore to separate it from the waste rock accompanying it.

OUTCROP
The line where a lode reaches the surface of the ground.

OXLAND PROCESS
An early chemical process for separating tin ore from tungsten ore, which were both heavy minerals not readily dealt with by normal gravitational methods.

PARALLEL MOTION
An ingenious arrangement for connecting the top of the piston rod of a Cornish pumping engine (which moved up and down in a straight line) with the inner end of the pump beam (which moved in an arc of a circle).

PELTON WHEEL
Water-driven power source consisting of a wheel with cups round its circumference acted on by a powerful jet of water issuing from a nozzle. Needed a head of water of 100 feet or more and speed of wheel could exceed 500 r.p.m.

PICKING HOUSE or -shed or -floor
Place where ore was sorted by hand.

PNEUMATIC STAMPS
See Stamps.

POWDER HOUSE
Store for explosives usually sited some distance from mine buildings, etc.

PRECIPITATING
See Copper Precipitating

PRODUCER GAS
Made by passing air and steam over a bed of glowing coal or other combustible matter to produce carbon monoxide and hydrogen. The air and steam were drawn through the producer by the induction strokes of the gas engine, hence the alternative term "suction gas".

PROSPECT
A trial excavation dug with a view to starting up a mine.

P.S.I.
Pressure in pounds per square inch.

PULP or pulped ore
Pulverised ore usually carried along by running water from one ore-dressing device to another.

PULSOMETER
Rudimentary steam device for pumping from very shallow mines merely consisting of two chambers, two non-return valves and a differential valve.

PULVERISER or Grinder
Machine, of which many varieties existed, for reducing ore to a finely divided state.

PUMP COLUMN
Large iron pipe, consisting of individual sections bolted one to another for conveying water up a shaft to surface or to adit level.

PUMP ROD
Wooden or metal rod connected to a power source at surface down to a pump in the shaft. See also Balance Box.

PYROLUSITE
Manganese dioxide, MnO_2, principal manganese ore in the district.

RABBLING
Stirring ore being roasted in a furnace. See Ch. 6.

RACK FRAME or Ragging Frame
A development of the square buddle which was continuous-acting so could work unattended.

RAFT WHEEL or Dipper Wheel or Elevator
Sometimes spelt Raff. In effect a waterwheel in reverse, which if turned by mechanical means would raise up waterborne pulped ore so that it could be put through the ore-dressing processes a second time.

REFINED ARSENIC
See Arsenic.

REFINING FURNACE
A simple furnace in which crude arsenic, or "arsenic soot" was roasted again, fumes from which were condensed to produce pure "white arsenic". See Ch. 11.

REVERBERATORY FURNACE
See Calciner.

REVOLVING SLIME TABLE
See Slime Table.

RINKLE
Burnt residue from roasting ore in calciner or other furnace.

ROCK BREAKER
See Crusher.

ROCK DRILL or Machine Drill
Mechanical drill, usually worked by compressed air, for boring holes in rock for the placing of blasting charges.

ROCKER BOB or Rocker Beam or Bob or Beam
Massive pivotted beam connected at one end to a power source, e.g. piston rod of a steam engine and at the other to a line of pump rods in a shaft, or to a crank if rotary motion was required.

ROD MILL
A modern gyratory rock breaker.

ROLLS or Cornish Rolls
Parallel revolving rollers between which ore was crushed when fine crushing was not needed.

ROUND FRAME
A development of the circular buddle in which the bed itself revolved, pulp being fed onto it at one point, waste was washed off at a second point and concentrated ore at a third point, so that it was continuous-acting.

R.P.M.
Revolutions per minute.

SCREEN
Perforated metal or woven wire sieve, either vibrating rectangular or revolving cylindrical, for sizing ore fragments. See Ch. 2.

SETT
The area of ground owned or leased by a mine.

SETTLING PIT or Settling Tank
Tank, usually rectangular and of concrete, where waterborne ore could settle and be dug out after the water accompanying it had been drained off. See Ch. 7.

SHAFT
More or less vertical entrance to a mine. Could be for pumping from (usually termed Engine Shaft), for hoisting from (sometimes termed a Whim Shaft), for access by ladders (termed Footway Shaft), or for ventilation.

SHAFT COLLAR
Timber or masonry structure round top of shaft to prevent loose ground collapsing inwards.

SHAKING TABLE
See Concentrating Table.

SHEAR LEGS
Timber structure at shaft head carrying a pulley, used for raising or lowering heavy equipment in the shaft.

SLIME POND or Lagoon.
Pond where waste slime could be settled rather than be carried into neighbouring rivers.

SLIME TABLE.
Round Frame or Concentrating Table designed to deal specifically with slimes.

SLIMES
Ore so finely divided as to be difficult to recover completely.

SLUICE BOX or Strip
Long wooden launder with low crosspieces placed at intervals along the bottom of it. Ore and waste was allowed to flow along it in suspension, heavy particles tending to settle against the crosspieces while water and lighter material flowed over them. See Ch. 7.

SKIP
See Cage.

SOLLAR
Wooden platform in or over a shaft. When mines were abandoned shafts were sometimes "sollared over" and the sollar covered with rubble, making such sites dangerous today with the rotting of the sollars with consequent risk of collapse into the shaft.

SOOT
See Arsenic.

SPALLING
Breaking up large pieces of ore with sledge hammers.

SPRINKLER
See Wash Tower.

STAMPS
Devices for crushing lode material to the consistency of sand as a first step towards separating mineral ore from waste rock. Various types existed (Cornish, Californian, Holman's Pneumatic, etc.) the simplest form amounting to vertical stems or "lifters" with their lower ends heavily shod with iron, each being alternately lifted by pegs on a revolving drum and allowed to drop on material in a mortar box.

STOPE, Stoping
Excavation of ore underground was referred to as stoping and the place where it was carried out as a stope. Removing ore from the roof of the stope was referred to as overhand or back stoping while taking it from the floor (the less usual method) as underhand stoping.

STRIP
See Sluice Box.

STULL
Working platform or staging erected to facilitate access to the upper part of a stope.

TABLE
See Concentrating Table.

TAIL RACE
Leat or conduit taking water away from a waterwheel, etc.

TAILINGS or Tails
The poorer product from an ore-dressing device, as opposed to the richer product, the "Heads".

TIN FLOORS
See Dressing Floors.

TIN ORE
See Cassiterite.

TRAMROAD or Tramway
Narrow gauge mine railway, either above or below ground.

TROMMEL
Revolving sieve for sizing ore fragments. See Ch. 2.

TUNGSTEN ORE
See Wolfram.

SUCTION GAS
See Producer Gas.

TURBINE or Water Turbine
Power source in which a flow of water was used to turn an enclosed spindle to which vanes were attached. Could be designed to work from a head of water of only a foot or so up to several hundred feet at rotor speeds of about 40 r.p.m. upwards.

TURNBOB or Angle Bob
Arrangement for changing the direction of flat rods or pump rods, resembling a large bell crank. See Ch. 5.

UMBER
Earthy brown ore containing iron and manganese and used for paint manufacture, etc.

VANNER
See Frue Vanner.

VANNING SHOVEL
A special shovel with a rather broad flat blade used by prospectors or as a ready means of checking the products of ore-dressing appliances. Water and crushed material are put on the blade which is then given a combined jerking and swirling motion which causes the heavier particles to separate out from the waste.

WASH TOWER
A chamber between the end of an arsenic flue and the stack containing blocks of limestone kept wet by water from a sprinkler and intended to reduce the emission of noxious gases from the stack.

WATER TURBINE
See Turbine.

WATERWHEEL
Common source of power, in use in almost every traditional mine and usually of the "overshot" variety, water being fed to the upper part of the wheel, its weight in the "buckets" causing the wheel to revolve. Speed of rotation slow — up to 15 r.p.m. for small wheels down to only 4 r.p.m. or so in the biggest. Made in all sizes, up to 50 or more feet in diameter.

WHEAL
Prefix meaning mine which in earlier days was spelt Huel.

WHEELPIT
Masonry pit in which a waterwheel was sited.

WHIM or Hoist or Winder
Machine for hoisting from a shaft, Whim being the older term, driven by any convenient power source, and usually provided with an indicator so that the engineman could be kept aware of the position of the cage in the shaft.

WINZE
Vertical shaft within a mine, but not extending to surface.

WOLFRAM
Tungsten ore, tungstate of iron and manganese, $(Fe,Mn)WO_4$, the chief source of tungsten in the district.

ZIRCON
Zirconium silicate, $ZrSiO_4$, a principal source of zirconium, which has a number of uses in industry, including the nuclear industry. Transparent varieties are used as gemstones.

BIBLIOGRAPHY

The works listed in the bibliography are restricted to those published after 1913 but study has also embraced earlier standard publications on West Country mining. These included, among many others, the official Mineral Statistics from 1848, Geological Survey District Memoirs in respect of Exeter (1902), Plymouth & Liskeard (1907), Tavistock & Launceston (1911), Dartmoor (1912), Ivybridge (1912) and Newton Abbot (1913), together with J.H. Collins' classic *West of England Mining Region* of 1912. In addition the 2nd Edition Ordnance Survey Six Inches to the Mile maps, published between 1904 and 1907, have been used extensively.

ATKINSON B. *Mining sites in Devon & Cornwall* (Dyllansow Truran) 1988

ATKINSON M. & SCHMITZ C.J. *Kelly Mine* (Devon Historian) 1975

ATKINSON M. & OTHERS *Dartmoor Mines* (University of Exeter) 1978

BARCLAY C.F. & OTHERS Reports on local mines (unpublished MSS) 1918-40

BARCLAY C.F. & OTHERS *The West Devon Mining District* (Trans. Royal Geological Society of Cornwall) 1930

BARTON D.B. *Copper Mining in Cornwall* (Truro Bookshop) 1961

BARTON D.B. *Mines & Mineral Railways of E. Cornwall & W. Devon* (D.B. Barton Ltd.) 1964

BARTON D.B. *The Cornish Beam Engine* (D.B. Barton Ltd.) 1969

BAWDEN M. *The Tavistock Mining District* (Trans. Devonshire Association) 1914

BOOKER F.L. *Industrial Archaeology of the Tamar Valley* (David & Charles) 1967

BROUGHTON D.G. *Birch Tor & Vitifer Mines* (Trans. Cornish Institute of Engineers) 1968

BURT R. & OTHERS *Devon & Somerset Mines* (University of Exeter) 1984

BURT R. & OTHERS *Cornish Mines* (University of Exeter) 1987

CORNISH CHAMBER OF MINES Annual Reports 1918-21

CORNISH CHAMBER OF MINES *Mining in Cornwall Today* 1974

GEOLOGICAL SURVEY Special Reports on Mineral Resources — Copper; Unbedded Iron Ores; Barytes; Fluorspar; Molybdenite; Arsenic & Antimony; Lead, Silver-lead & Zinc; Tungsten & Manganese; (no report on Tin Ore was published) (H.M.S.O.) 1917-23

GEOLOGICAL SURVEY *Metalliferous Mining Region of S.W. England* by H.G. Dines (H.M.S.O.) 1956

GEOLOGICAL SURVEY *Geology of Okehampton* (H.M.S.O.) 1968

GOODRIDGE J.C. *Devon Great Consols* (Trans. Devonshire Association) 1964

GREEVES T.A.P. *Tin Mines & Miners of Dartmoor* (Devon Books) 1986

HARRIS H. *Industrial Archaeology of Dartmoor* (David & Charles) 1968

JENKIN A.K.H. *The Cornish Miner* (Allen & Unwin) 1927

JENKIN A.K.H. *Cornwall's Mines & Miners* (Geographical Magazine) 1937

JENKIN A.K.H. *Mines & Miners of Cornwall — St. Austell to Saltash* (Truro Bookshop) 1967

JENKIN A.K.H. *Mines & Miners of Cornwall — Calstock &c.* (Federation of Old Cornwall Societies) 1969

JENKIN A.K.H. *Mines of Devon — Southern Area* (David & Charles) 1974

JENKIN A.K.H. *Mines of Devon — N. & E. of Dartmoor* (Devon Library Services) 1981

NUNNEY R.S. *Any Old Iron? — Great Rock Mine* (Devon Life) 1970

MESSENGER M. *Bulkamore Mine* (Industrial Railway Record) 1977

MOOR C.G. *Tin Mining* (Pitman) 1928

PERKINS J.W. *Geology Explained — S. & E. Devon* (David & Charles) 1971

PERKINS J.W. *Geology Explained - Dartmoor & Tamar Valley* (David & Charles) 1972.

RAMSDEN J.V. *Notes on the Mines of Devonshire* (Trans. Devonshire Association) 1952

ROBINS J.A.C. *Follow the Leat* (Published privately) 1984

ROBINS J.A.C. *Rambling On* (John Pegg Publishing) 1988

SCHMITZ C.J. *Teign Valley Lead Mines* (Northern Mine Research Society) 1972

TERRELL E. Wheal Jewell & Marytavy Mines 1914

TOLL R.W. *Arsenic in W. Devon & E. Cornwall* (Sands, Clays & Minerals) 1938

TOLL R.W. *Copper recovery from low-grade waters at Devon Great Consols* (Mining Magazine) 1946

TOLL R.W. *Radioactive minerals in the Tavistock District* (Mining Magazine) 1951

TROUNSON J.H. *Some useful prospects in Cornwall* (Mining Magazine) 1951

TROUNSON J.H. *Mining in Cornwall* (Moorland Publishing) 1960

VILLAGERS OF HOLNE *History of Holne* (St. Nicholas Books) 1977

Other publications included:-

Annual Official Lists of Active Mines (H.M.S.O.)

Catalogue of Plans of Abandoned Mines (H.M.S.O.) 1929

Report of the Mineral Development Committee (H.M.S.O.) 1949

Journals of the Plymouth Mineral & Mining Club

Tamar, the Journal of the Friends of Morwellham

Transactions of the Devonshire Association

Proceedings of the Teign Naturalists Field Society

Western Morning News files

Totnes Times files

Errata to 1995 reprint

Page 26	line 5 delete fullstop after "killed"
Page 28	line 10 for "South" read "S.E."
Page 36	line 19 for "of mine" read "of the mine"
Page 51	line 12 after "Okehampton" delete "road"
Page 70	Plumley, line 4 for "side the" read "side of the"
Page 93	line 19 for "wheelpits" read "wheelpit"
Page 108	line 15 for "Wheal Maria" read "Wheal Anna Maria"
Page 130	Calstock & Danescombe, line 1 for "330 yards" read "800 yards"
Page 131	Danescombe & Consolidated Tamar, Grid Reference, for "422695" read "426696" and line 1 for "330 yards" read "800 yards"
Page 137	Silver Valley, line 2 after "work done" delete "by"
Page 140	lines 2 and 3 for "with the last surviving Cornish mines closing down" read "with the last surviving Cornish mine but one closing down"